CLASSIC
BIBLE
STORIES

Geoffrey Willis *is a full-time curate with the Church of England and organises youth programmes for local churches, schools, holiday camps and youth festivals. He holds two degrees: in Law and Theology.*

Mike Dodd *trained at the Chelsea School of Art in London. He taught art in schools and then became a full-time book illustrator. He has illustrated several children's books.*

First published in 1989 by
The Hamlyn Publishing Group Limited
Michelin House
81 Fulham Road
London SW3 6RB

CLASSIC
BIBLE
STORIES

RETOLD FOR TODAY'S CHILD

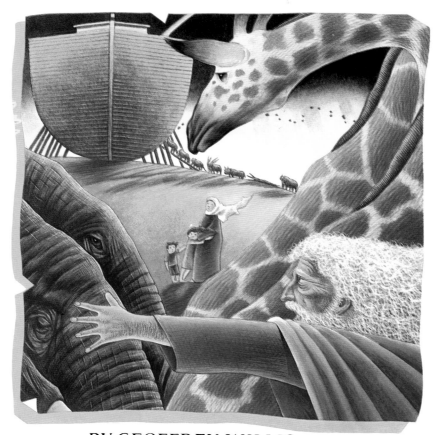

BY GEOFFREY WILLIS

ILLUSTRATED BY MIKE DODD

HAMLYN

Contents

The Old Testament

The New Testament

God makes the world

Long, long ago, before time began, there was nothing but blackness. If you had been there, you would have seen nothing. There were no people, no animals, no plants. In fact, even the earth did not exist. There was nothing there at all. Nothing, that is, except God.

God made a huge ball of fire to warm up the blackness and to give light. He called it the sun. Then he made all the stars and the moon and the earth. On the earth, there was nothing but water. No land, just water – everywhere.

God said, 'I shall create a garden.' He pushed the water to one side and made land appear. On the land, he made trees and bushes, plants and flowers. God looked down and out of his eyes flashed colour. Instantly, the world was filled with blues and greens, reds and yellows.

God said, 'I shall make creatures to live in my garden.' He made animals of every size, shape and colour. Some crawled, some hopped, some walked and some skipped. Some were slow, like the snail, others as fast as the cheetah. God spoke and out of his mouth came noises for all the animals. And the world was filled with braying and quacking, mooing and barking. When he had made them all, God was very pleased.

God said, 'I shall make one more animal. He will be special. He will be like me.' God took some earth in his hands. Carefully, he moulded it until he had made a man. Gently, he leant down and kissed him and breathed his breath into the man. And the man became alive. God called the man Adam.

Adam loved the garden but he was unhappy.

'Why are you sad?' asked God.

'I feel lonely,' Adam replied. 'I love the animals but I long for someone to talk to.'

So God sent Adam into a deep sleep. He opened up the man's side and took out one rib. He used the rib to create a woman. Then he breathed life into the woman. God woke Adam.

'She is beautiful,' Adam cried. 'I feel we belong together.'

'You do,' said God. 'She is not like the animals who can't talk and are less intelligent than you are. She is equal to you. In fact, she is part of you. Together, you make a whole. Her name is Eve.'

So Adam and Eve lived together in the garden. They loved each other and they looked after the garden and all the animals. And everything was perfect . . . for a while.

Adam and Eve disobey God

Adam and Eve lived in the garden and were very happy. They were allowed to do anything they liked – except for one thing. God told them they were not allowed to eat the fruit from the tree in the middle of the garden. God wanted to see if the man and woman would love him enough to do as he asked, to obey him.

Now, the devil hated God. The devil was an angel who had become bad. He had led a revolt against God and been thrown out of heaven. The devil hated God and wanted to spoil anything that God had made. He knew that God loved the man and the woman. So he decided to try and hurt them and spoil God's world. The devil disguised himself as a snake. Putting on his smarmiest voice, he approached the woman. 'Nice day,' he said. 'Have you tried the fruit on the tree in the middle of the garden? I can recommend it. It's absolutely delicious.'

'We're not allowed to eat it,' Eve replied.

'Why on earth not?' jeered the serpent. 'It's lovely.'

'God said we mustn't or we'll die.'

'Rubbish!' laughed the devil. 'You won't die. The fruit from that tree will make you as powerful and clever as God – and he doesn't want that.'

'Well,' hesitated Eve, 'I don't know.'

'Just try it,' urged the devil. 'One bite can't do you any harm.'

So Eve took a fruit from the tree and bit into it. Then she rushed and told Adam and he ate some too. Just then, they heard the voice of God calling them. They both went red with guilt and ran and hid. But God found them. 'Why were you hiding?' God asked. 'Have you done something wrong?'

'It was her fault,' cried Adam. 'She made me eat some of the forbidden fruit.'

'She *made* you? Is she stronger than you then? Did she force you?' God turned to Eve. 'Why did you disobey me?' he asked.

'It was the snake's fault – he made me eat.'

'*Made* you?' asked God. 'Did he force you?' God turned to both of them, sadly. 'No one *made* you eat. You both chose to disobey me. Because you disobeyed me, you cannot stay in this beautiful garden and you will die.' They gasped. 'Because you disobeyed me, death has come into the world. But don't despair. You will not die forever. I will make sure that the devil will not win. One day, I will rescue you – defeat death and bring you back to life.'

And God led Adam and Eve out of the beautiful garden to begin their new life in the wide world.

Noah builds a boat

Adam and Eve had children, grandchildren, great-grandchildren and soon the world was full of people. God looked down on the beautiful world he had made and was sad. Instead of looking after it, people were spoiling it. 'People are selfish,' thought God. 'They're cruel to the animals and they don't look after my world.' One man was different, however. He loved God and cared for the earth. His name was Noah.

'Noah,' God said, one day, 'I am going to stop these evil people before they destroy my world. I will flood the whole earth. You must build a boat – call it the Ark. Take on board two of every kind of animal. You, your family and these animals will be the only ones to survive the flood.'

'Two of *every* animal?' asked Noah.

'Yes – from cockroaches to camels!' God replied. 'The Ark must be tall enough for giraffes, strong enough for elephants, with cubbyholes for caterpillars and butterflies. And don't forget food for them all,' added God, gently.

'It'll have to be a big boat,' said Noah.

'Not big,' said God. '*Huge!* So I should start right away.'

Noah set to work. He chopped down trees, sawed them up and made the frame. It took him weeks – he got blisters and splinters galore. The people made fun of him but Noah kept on working. Eventually, it was finished.

'It looks like a barn,' his friends laughed, 'only bigger!'

'Actually, it's a boat,' said Noah. They roared with laughter.

'Forgotten something?' they jeered. 'Where's the water?'

'That's coming,' said Noah and he explained about the flood.

'What rot!' they cried. 'We'll believe it when we see it.'

'It will be too late by then,' said Noah, sadly.

When the animals arrived, the people laughed even more. 'Noah's opening a zoo!'

But Noah did not laugh – the rain had begun to fall. It fell all day, every day, for 40 days. The flood water rose – until finally it covered even the mountain tops. But the ark bobbed safely on the water's surface with all the animals inside. Then Noah sent out a dove which came back with an olive leaf. When the dove was sent out again, it did not return. Suddenly, there was a bump. They had hit dry land! All at once, the sky lit up with every colour you could ever imagine. It was a huge rainbow – the first they had ever seen.

'However hard it rains, I promise I will never flood the world again,' said God. 'The rainbow is to remind you of that promise. Now go and enjoy yourselves. And this time, please look after my world.'

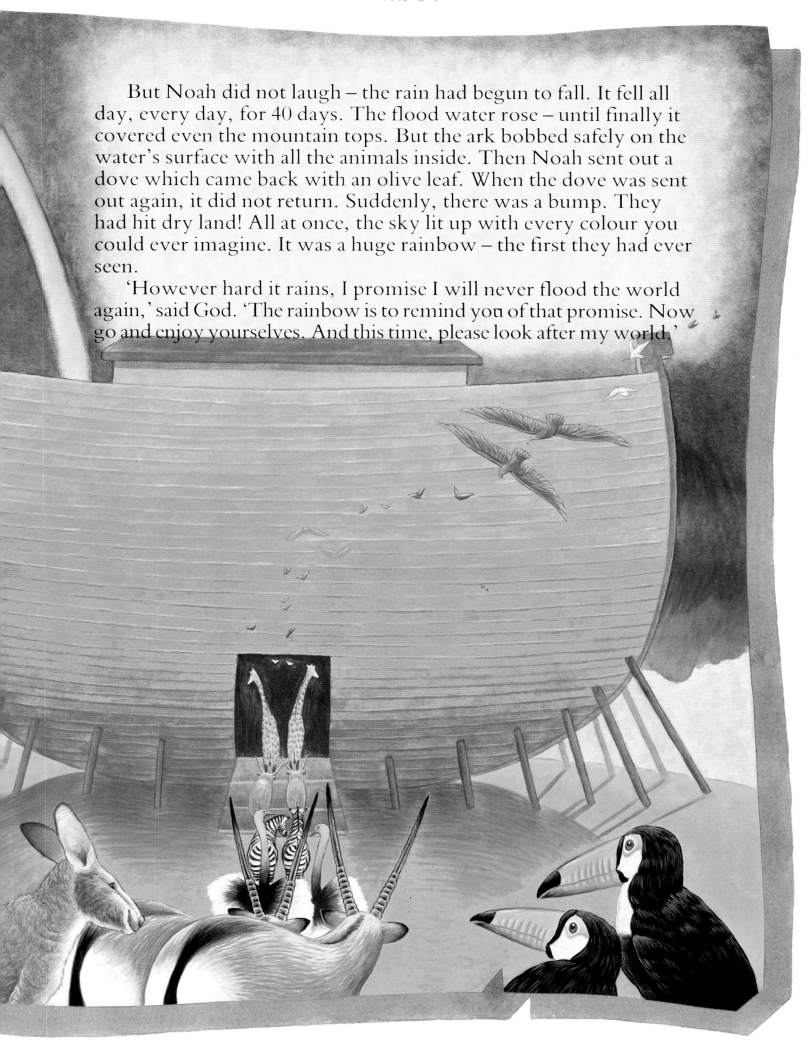

Abraham and the long, long journey

Noah was not the only one God sent on a journey . . .
Abraham went on one, too . . . and *he* didn't have a boat.
Abraham was 75 years old. He had loved and obeyed God
all his life. One day, God said to Abraham, 'Abraham, I want you
to go and live in a far-away country.'

'I'm too old for travelling,' thought Abraham. But what God
said next *really* shocked him.

'In that country, your family will grow to be as vast as the
number of stars in the sky.'

Abraham looked up and tried to work out just how many that
would be. But he quickly lost count. 'How can my family become
that big?' he thought, 'I don't even have a son.' But Abraham
knew better than to argue with God. So Abraham packed
his belongings and set off with his wife, Sarah. There were
no removal vans to help in those days so it took them
ages to travel anywhere. Abraham had so many
sheep, goats and cows. And, what's more, they
didn't even know where they were going.

'Perhaps this is the place?' said Abraham,
each time they stopped, hoping he
could put his feet up at last. But,
each time, God told him to keep
going. They walked through
the mountains. 'Perhaps *this*
is the place?' But God said
to keep on moving.
They went down
to the plain.

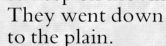

There was a famine there so they journeyed on to Egypt and stayed with the King until the famine had passed. On and on they went. Once, one of Abraham's relatives was kidnapped by four evil Kings. So Abraham formed his servants into an army and rescued him. But still they kept on going.

'It's not time to stop,' said God. 'You can't put your feet up yet.'

They travelled for miles and miles and years and years; 24 years to be exact! Until, at last, they arrived at the very highest point in the mountains. 'This is your new home,' said God, at last.

But Abraham was sad. 'It doesn't feel like home because I don't have any children to live in it.'

God smiled at Abraham, 'You will have a son. And your son will give you grandsons and they will give you great-grandsons . . . and, in time, your family will grow so large, they will fill the country as far as your eyes can see!'

Abraham looked. He could see for miles and miles. It would have to be the biggest family ever! When his wife, Sarah, heard what God had said, she laughed. 'Abraham is 99 years old and I'm far too old to start having children!'

But God kept his promise. And all the stories in this book are about different members of Abraham's family, some grand-children, some great-grandchildren and some great-great-great, but, first . . . comes the story of Abraham's son, Isaac.

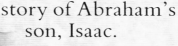

Abraham and Isaac

God kept his promise – Abraham was 100 years old when his son, Isaac, was born. Every morning, Abraham thanked God for all the good things God had given him. He thanked God for his wife, Sarah; for their new home; and, most of all, for their young son, Isaac.

One day, when Abraham was praying, God asked him a question. 'Abraham, do you love me?'

'Yes,' said Abraham.

'Do you love me more than anything and anybody else?'

'Yes,' said Abraham, again.

God decided to test Abraham. He wanted to see if Abraham really loved him most of all. He wanted to know if Abraham would trust him – no matter what happened. So God asked him, 'Will you always do what I ask?'

'Yes,' promised Abraham, 'you know I will.'

'Good,' said God. 'Then I want you to kill Isaac.' Abraham could hardly believe his ears. 'I want you to climb to the top of the mountain and to sacrifice Isaac to me.'

Tears welled up in Abraham's eyes. He loved Isaac very much and that was the last thing he wanted. But he knew that he had to obey God. He knew that whatever God said, however strange, God knew best. So Abraham loaded his donkey with wood and coal for the sacrifice and set off.

They hadn't gone far when, suddenly, Isaac stopped. 'Daddy, you've forgotten an animal for the sacrifice. I'll run back home and get a lamb.'

'No, Isaac. God is going to provide the lamb for the sacrifice,' said Abraham, biting his lip and trying not to cry.

They left the donkey at the foot of the mountain and climbed slowly to the top. Isaac helped his father build the altar, using the wood and the coals. When they had finished, he saw that Abraham was crying. 'Daddy, what's the matter?' he asked.

Abraham didn't answer. Gently, he tied Isaac's hands behind his back and laid the boy on the top of the altar. He took out his knife ready to kill his only son. Suddenly, a loud voice blazed

across the mountain. 'Abraham! Don't touch the boy!' It was God's voice. 'Now I know you love me and obey me. You were even prepared to sacrifice your only son to me. Now, look.'

Abraham could hardly see through the tears, but there, caught in a thorn bush, was a ram. Abraham helped Isaac down off the altar and, together, they sacrificed the ram to God.

As they set off for home, Abraham smiled. He hadn't let God down – and God hadn't let him down. God had provided the sacrifice after all.

God finds a wife for Isaac

Abraham was now very old and Isaac, his son, was a grown man. One morning, Abraham called his servant and said, 'Before I die, I want to see my son, Isaac, happily married.'

'Well, there are plenty of beautiful women to choose from . . .' started his servant.

'No,' interrupted Abraham. 'None of them is good enough for my son. I want you to go to the country where I was born and find Isaac a wife.'

'But, but . . .' stammered the servant. 'What if I can't find one? What if she won't come with me? What if Isaac doesn't like her? What colour hair should she have and what if . . .?'

'Don't worry,' said Abraham. 'God will help you choose the perfect wife for Isaac.'

The servant set off. After a long, hard journey, he came to the country where Abraham had been born. He was tired and thirsty and stopped at a well to have a drink. 'How will I find a wife?' he thought.

Suddenly, God spoke to him. 'Ask the first woman who comes to the well for a drink. If she gives you a drink and offers to water your camels, then that is the girl Isaac is to marry.'

So the servant waited. Soon, a girl arrived. She was very beautiful. 'Please may I have a drink from your well?' he asked.

'Certainly. Shall I give your camels some water, too?'

The servant gave her a beautiful gold ring. 'God has chosen you to marry Isaac,' he explained.

'You'd better come home and meet my parents,' she said.

So they went to her house. The servant began to explain all about his journey.

'Well, Rebecca,' asked the girl's father, after hearing the story, 'will you marry Isaac?'

'Yes,' she said. 'God works in funny ways. But I'm sure he knows best.'

As he travelled back with Rebecca, the servant was worried – would Isaac like her? But when Isaac saw Rebecca, he didn't just like her – he loved her.

'How did you find such a beautiful wife?' he asked the servant.

'Easy,' the servant smiled. 'God arranged the whole thing!'

The troublesome twins

Soon after she married Isaac, Rebecca became pregnant. 'I know babies kick,' she said, one day, 'but it feels like there's a wrestling match going on inside me!'

'It must be twins,' laughed Isaac.

Sure enough, Rebecca had twin boys. The first boy was red and hairy and the second came out holding on to the ankle of the first. 'They really have been fighting,' said Isaac.

They named them, Esau and Jacob. Although they were twins, they were totally different. Esau, the eldest, was strong and loved to go hunting. Jacob was quieter and stayed at home, helping his mother, Rebecca. The two boys were always fighting. Esau won every time because he was much stronger and he bullied Jacob. But Jacob was cleverer. 'One day, I'll get my own back,' he vowed.

Now, Esau had one big fault. He was a glutton – a real pig. He adored food. One day, after he had been hunting, he returned, ravenously hungry. Jacob

was cooking soup and the smell was delicious.

'Give me some soup,' Esau demanded.

'Only if you give me something in return,' taunted Jacob.

'Anything you like,' Esau promised.

'Give me your rights as the eldest son,' said Jacob. As the eldest son, Esau would one day inherit his father's wealth and be given a special blessing by him. 'Done,' said Esau and gobbled up the soup.

Meanwhile, Rebecca, who had been watching this, thought to herself, 'Esau doesn't deserve to receive his father's property and blessing if he is prepared to give it away for a bowl of soup!' And she began to plan and scheme.

One day, Isaac called Esau into his room. 'I'm about to die,' he said. 'I want to give you my special blessing. Fetch me my favourite food and then I will bless you.' So Esau went out hunting.

'Quickly,' Rebecca said to Jacob. 'You must get your father's blessing instead of that good-for-nothing glutton, Esau.'

'But my father will recognize me.'

'Your father is nearly blind!' laughed Rebecca. 'Wear these goatskins on your arms. Isaac will feel that you are hairy and think you are Esau.'

So Jacob put on goatskins and, dressed up in his brother's clothes, he carried the stew into his father. Isaac reached out and touched Jacob. When he felt the goatskins, he thought that it was Esau. So he gave Jacob his special blessing.

Esau returned to find he had been tricked. He was furious. 'You wait until I get hold of my little brother!' But Jacob ran and hid. He had won; he had outsmarted his big brother and cheated him out of his father's blessing.

Joseph has a dream

Jacob grew up and had 12 sons and a daughter. Joseph was the second youngest and he was his father's favourite. He was not very popular with his brothers. When his father, Jacob, gave him a beautiful multi-coloured coat, for instance, they were very jealous. But it was Joseph's dreams that made his brothers really mad. Every morning, when Joseph came down to breakfast, he would tell them in great detail what he'd dreamt the night before. 'Boring!' they would mutter under their breath and try to ignore him. But one morning, Joseph really went too far.

'Last night, I dreamt that we were all gathering in the corn when, suddenly, all your bundles bowed down to mine!' he declared. His brothers bit their lips, seething with rage.

The next morning it was even worse. 'Last night, I dreamt that the sun and the moon and 11 stars bowed down to me,' he said. This time, even his father, Jacob, was cross. 'If you think that your mother and I are like the sun and the moon and that we're going to bow down to you – you're mistaken!'

'I was only telling you my dream,' said Joseph and his brothers began to hate him more and more.

One day, Jacob sent Joseph to see how his brothers were getting on, tending the sheep. Joseph strutted along in his brightly-coloured coat. His brothers recognized him from a long way off.

'We've had enough of his dreams,' they complained and began to plan how to get rid of him. Reuben wanted to protect Joseph so, instead of killing him, they threw Joseph down a disused well. As they were walking away, they saw a caravan of slave traders approaching. His brothers quickly pulled Joseph out of the well and sold him into slavery for 20 pieces of silver. They took his coat and dipped it in the blood of a sheep. 'We'll tell Jacob we found his coat and that he must have been eaten by a wild animal.'

'That's the last of him and his dreams,' they laughed.

But they were wrong.

Joseph's dream comes true

Joseph was taken to Egypt by the slave traders and sold as a slave. Many years passed but, whatever happened, Joseph trusted God. The wife of Joseph's master, Potiphar, was jealous of Joseph, so she lied about him and he was thrown in prison. While he was in prison, two officials were jailed by Pharaoh, King of Egypt: Pharaoh's wine-waiter and his baker. One morning, they came to Joseph. 'I dreamt I squeezed three bunches of grapes into Pharaoh's cup,' said the wine waiter. 'What does it mean?'

'It means that in three days you'll get your job back.'

'I dreamt I was carrying three baskets of pastries and the birds were eating them,' said the baker.

Joseph looked sad. 'It means that in three days Pharaoh will have you hanged.' Three days later, both dreams came true. The wine waiter got his job back and the baker was hanged.

Months later, Pharaoh had a dream. He called his experts, advisers and magicians but none of them could tell him the meaning of his dream. 'Quick, fetch me a drink, before I lose my temper and have you all hanged!' screamed Pharaoh. Suddenly the wine waiter remembered Joseph and brought him from prison.

'I dreamt,' Pharaoh told Joseph, 'that there were seven huge fat cows but seven skinny cows ate them up. Then I saw seven big grains of corn but seven thin grains ate them up. What does it mean?' Joseph explained that it meant there would be seven good years with plenty to eat. Then seven years of famine. Food should be stored in the good years so there would be enough to eat in the seven bad years. Pharaoh was so impressed, he appointed Joseph governor over all of Egypt. For seven years, he stored food and, when famine struck, there was plenty to eat in Egypt. Back in Canaan, however, Jacob and his sons were starving so they had to travel to Egypt for food. When they arrived, they did not recognize Joseph. They bowed down and asked him for food. Joseph smiled – his dream had come true. Then he began to cry – tears of happiness. In spite of everything, he couldn't help loving them. 'Come and live in Egypt with me,' he told them.

So Jacob, and his whole family, came to live in Egypt. Over the years, the family grew into a tribe called the Israelites. And, for many years, they lived happily in Egypt.

Moses is born

After Joseph and all his brothers had died, their descendants, the Israelites, continued to live happily in Egypt.

Eventually, however, a new Pharaoh came to power. He was an evil man who hated the Israelites and treated them cruelly.

One day, a seven-year-old Israelite girl, called Miriam, found her mother crying. 'What's the matter?' she asked.

'I'm going to have a baby.'

'Then why are you crying? I've always wanted a baby brother or sister. Just wait until all my friends hear about it.'

'Ssh,' whispered her mother. 'You mustn't tell anyone. Pharaoh has ordered that all Israelite baby boys must be thrown into the River Nile and killed. If I have a boy and the Egyptian soldiers find out, they'll take him away.'

Miriam and her family did everything possible to keep it a secret. At last the baby was born . . . it was a boy. For three months they managed to keep the baby hidden. But, every time he cried, they had to sing or pretend to have an argument to drown the noise. Soon, it became impossible.

'We can't hide him any longer,' Miriam's father said, one night. So, in the morning, Miriam's mother took a basket made of reeds. Her father covered it with tar to make it water-tight and they placed the baby inside. Miriam and her mother carried the basket down to the water's edge and floated it on the River Nile. Miriam's mother could not bear to watch and she ran home, weeping. But Miriam stayed, watching the basket float on the river. 'Dear God,' she prayed, 'please look after my little brother.'

Just at that moment, Pharaoh's daughter came down to the river to bathe. She saw the basket and sent a slave to fetch it for her. When she opened it, she realized it was one of the Israelite babies. Miriam watched in terror. What would happen?

'I will adopt him as my own son,' said Pharaoh's daughter. 'I shall call him Moses.'

Miriam could hardly believe her ears. She rushed forward – she'd had a brainwave. 'Excuse me, your majesty, but shall I fetch you a nanny to look after him? I know just the person for the job.'

Pharaoh's daughter agreed and Miriam ran to fetch her mother.

'Look after him,' said the Pharaoh's daughter. 'And, when he is old enough, he can come and live with me in the palace.'

So Miriam and her mother went home, carrying Moses. Miriam's baby brother was safe. God had answered her prayer.

Moses gets a new job

Moses did indeed go to live in Pharaoh's palace, for a short time. When he grew up, he left Egypt and married a girl called Zipporah and he started work as a shepherd, looking after his father-in-law's sheep.

One day, walking in the hills, he saw a bush on fire. 'That's odd,' he thought. 'The bush is blazing furiously but the leaves are still green. It's on fire – but it's not going black!'

Now, Moses was an inquisitive chap – some people might even have called him nosey. So he went over to take a closer look.

Suddenly, a voice boomed out. 'Moses, take your shoes off. You are treading on holy ground.' Moses kicked his shoes off instantly. He didn't dare look up – he knew it must be God speaking.

'Moses,' said God, 'I've got a job for you.'

'Th..th..thanks very much but I've g..g..got a job, looking after these sheep,' stammered Moses, nervously.

'I want you to look after my people. I want you to be a shepherd to them – to lead them out of Egypt to freedom in a new country.'

'You must have made a m..m..mistake. You must have the wrong man.'

'There's no mistake,' said God. 'Moses, I want you to go and talk to Pharaoh.'

'Me?' cried Moses. 'Go to the K..K..King of Egypt? You must be joking.'

'I am perfectly serious. Go and tell the King that I am angry at the way he's treating the Israelites. Tell him to free my people.'

'But he'll never believe I've really spoken to God.'

'That staff in your hand – throw it on the ground,' said God.
Moses did so – the instant it touched the ground, it turned into a snake. Moses leapt back two feet. He didn't like snakes.

'Pick it up by its tail,' said God.

Moses did not dare disobey God. Gingerly, he reached out – as soon as he touched the snake, it turned back into a stick.

'Wow,' thought Moses, 'that's something! But supposing he still doesn't believe me?' he asked God.

'Put your hand inside your cloak.' Moses did so – when he pulled it out, it was covered in white spots.

'Euch,' Moses shrieked, 'I've got the plague.' But when he put his hand back inside the coat, the spots vanished.

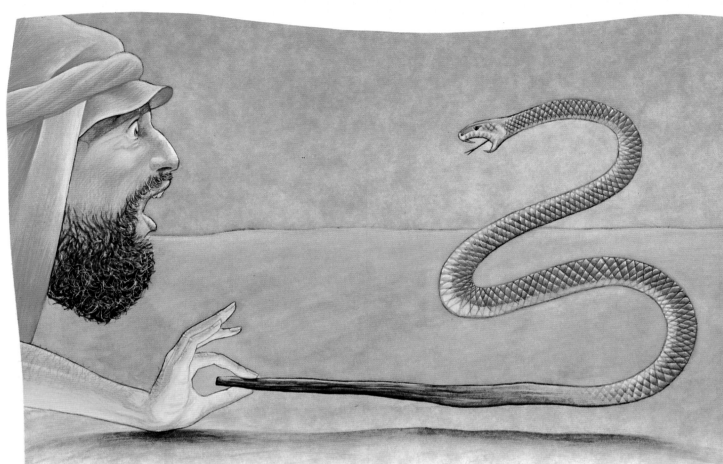

'If he still doesn't believe you, take some water from the River Nile and pour it on the ground. It'll turn into blood. That will convince him,' said God. 'Now hurry up and go.'

'Oh p..p..please don't send me. I'm n..n..not very good at t..t..talking,' Moses stammered. 'Can't you get someone else?'

'Moses, who made your mouth?'

'You did.'

'Who made your lips and your tongue?'

'You did.'

'Well, if I made them, then I know how they work, don't I? I'll help you talk.'

Moses was getting desperate. The thought of talking to Pharaoh was bringing on a migraine. 'Please can't you find someone better than me?' he pleaded. 'I'm hopeless at making speeches. In fact, I've never made one before – and certainly never to a pharoah.'

Then God was cross with Moses. 'Very well,' he said, 'take your brother, Aaron, with you.'

So Moses finally agreed to go. He was still terrified but at least, he thought, he wouldn't be alone – Aaron would be with him.

Of course, what he had forgotten all along was that God was going to be with him. God would be there helping him to know what to say. You see, when God asks you to do a job – it might be difficult – but he'll always help you do it.

God teaches Pharaoh a lesson

Moses and his brother, Aaron, were shown into the throne room of Pharaoh, the King of Egypt. 'Yes,' boomed the King of Egypt, 'What do you want?'

'Your majesty,' Moses began, 'you must let the Israelites go into the desert to worship God.' Pharaoh let out an ear-splitting laugh. Moses shivered. This was worse than he had imagined – and that had been bad enough.

'You obviously don't have enough work to do. Get out!' shouted Pharaoh and he gave the Israelites extra work.

'You see! He didn't believe me,' Moses complained to God. 'Now things are even worse.'

'Go and tell him again,' said God.

The second time, the King looked even more annoyed. 'What do you want this time?' he moaned.

'God says stop treating the Israelites as slaves. Let them go and worship him.'

'Nonsense!' Pharaoh cried. 'This God of yours doesn't exist.'
'Oh yes he does,' said Moses.

'Prove it,' snapped Pharaoh. So Moses threw his staff on the ground and it turned into a snake.

'Huh,' laughed Pharaoh's magicians and they did exactly the same thing. Moses was uncomfortable with all those snakes wriggling around. But, when his snake ate up all the magicians' snakes, he felt a little better. And, when he picked up his snake, it became a stick again.

'I don't believe in your God,' shouted Pharaoh. 'Get out before I have you thrown out!' Moses and Aaron left quickly.

'What now?' Moses asked God.

'Go back to Pharaoh. Each time he says no, I will give a sign to prove that I'm real. Eventually, he will let you go.'

So Moses returned to Pharaoh and told him, 'God says let the Israelites go.'

'No,' said Pharaoh.

So God turned the River Nile into blood. All the fish died and there was no water to drink or to wash in. But still the Pharaoh would not let them go. So God sent thousands of frogs. They got everywhere – in food, in clothes, even in the beds. 'Get rid of the frogs and I'll let you go,' promised Pharaoh. But, once the frogs had gone, he changed his mind.

God sent gnats. They got everywhere – in people's mouths and

up their noses. They buzzed all night. Pharaoh could not sleep. But still he would not let them go. Next, God sent flies. There were flies everywhere. 'Get rid of the flies and I'll let you go,' Pharaoh promised. But, once the flies had gone, he changed his mind.

God killed all the Egyptian cattle. Still Pharaoh would not let them go. God sent an epidemic of boils. All the Egyptians got them – in fact, Pharaoh had such a boily bottom he could not sit down. But still he would not let them go. God sent a thunderstorm, with hail as big as golf balls. Pharaoh's advisers begged him to let the Israelites go, before the whole country was destroyed.

At last, Pharaoh agreed. But, as soon as the storm passed, he changed his mind. God sent locusts. They ate everything. But still Pharaoh would not let them go. So God sent darkness. For three days it was so dark you could not see your own nose. Finally, Pharaoh called Moses. He was in a huge rage. 'Go!' he shouted.

'We must take all our possessions with us,' said Moses.

Pharaoh nearly went purple. 'No, you can't go,' he said, changing his mind. 'Get out of my sight! I never want to see you again!'

'Very well,' agreed Moses, 'but there will be one last plague. The angel of death will pass over Egypt and all your first born sons will die.' And, with that, Moses and Aaron walked out. Pharaoh was one person they would not mind never seeing again.

The escape through the Red Sea

Moses called all the Israelites together. 'Tonight,' he told them, 'God will give one final sign to force Pharaoh to let us go. Tomorrow, we shall leave Egypt for ever.' There was a huge cheer. 'Listen carefully,' Moses continued. 'We have a lot to do. Each family must take a lamb and kill it. Use the blood of the lamb to paint a mark on the doorposts of your homes and then stay indoors. During the night, the angel of death will come and kill every first born son. All the houses which are marked with the blood of the lamb will be safe. The angel of death will pass over those houses and will not harm anyone inside them.'

The Israelites went home and did just as Moses had said. They killed a lamb and put the blood on the doorposts. Then they had a big feast to celebrate and ate the lamb. They were very happy. All the years of slavery were over, they were going to be free at last. This was a night to remember. The feasting continued for hours.

In the very middle of the night, the angel of death struck. The Egyptians found all their first born sons dead. Pharaoh sent a message to Moses telling him the Israelites were now free to go.

It was still pitch dark when Moses gave the order to leave. The women were in the middle of baking bread to eat on the journey. So they took the dough, put it in their bags and marched off

into the night. They walked all night.

However, the next morning, Pharaoh changed his mind. He sent his army and chariots after the Israelites to force them to come back. When the Israelites saw they were being followed, they marched faster. But the Egyptian chariots were gaining fast. They were nearly on top of them when, suddenly, the Israelites froze in their tracks. They had reached the edge of the Red Sea. Everyone started to panic.

'We'll either drown or be killed by the Egyptians,' they screamed.

Moses cried to God in desperation, 'What shall I do now? We're trapped.'

'Raise your staff,' came the reply. Moses did as God said.

Instantly, the water of the Red Sea parted. A path, with towering walls of water on either side, stretched through the sea in front of them. The Israelites were stunned into silence. Quickly, they followed Moses into the sea. The Egyptian chariots followed close behind them.

As the last of the Israelites reached the other side, Moses raised his staff again. The walls of water rushed back together. The path and all the Egyptians on it disappeared under the sea. A huge cheer rose – almost as loud as the crashing of the waves.

They were safe at last . . . but there was a long way to go before they would finally reach their new home, the Promised Land.

The desert journey

Moses and the Israelites turned their backs on the Red Sea and set off into the desert. Each day, God went in front of them, leading them in a pillar of cloud to show them the way. Day after day, they followed the cloud. However, the food they had brought soon ran out and they became hungry.

'We were better off as slaves,' they grumbled to Moses. 'At least in Egypt we had food to eat!'

God heard the Israelites grumbling. 'Tomorrow, I shall make food fall from the sky,' he promised Moses. 'Tell the people to gather up only what they need for each day – but no more.'

The next morning, a flock of birds, called quails, landed all around the camp and there was dew everywhere. The Israelites ate the quails. When the dew dried, it left behind sticky stuff which they gathered and ate. It tasted like biscuits made of honey and they called it 'manna'. Some people disobeyed God's instructions and greedily gathered more than they needed. But it did them no good at all because the manna only lasted a day and, overnight, it went mouldy and became riddled with worms.

'The people must learn to obey me,' said God.

The Israelites kept on marching. It was so hot in the desert and there was no water. 'We might as well have stayed in Egypt!' they moaned to Moses. 'We're going to die of thirst!' So Moses prayed.

'Take your rod and strike that rock over there,' said God. Moses did so and water gushed from the rock. They drank their fill.

'The people must learn to trust me,' God said.

Eventually, they reached a mountain called Sinai. 'Moses, climb the mountain. I want to talk to you,' said God. So Moses climbed the mountain, while the Israelites stayed in the camp at the bottom. 'The people are very disobedient,' God said. 'Tell them they must keep these ten rules.' Then God wrote ten commandments on two huge blocks of stone and gave them to Moses.

When Moses came down from the mountain, he heard singing. The Israelites had made a golden calf and were bowing down and worshipping it. Moses was so furious he threw the stones on to the ground – they broke in half. 'How can you insult God and worship that lump of metal? God rescues you from the Egyptians, gives you food and water in the desert and you worship a metal cow!?'

Moses ordered the cow to be melted down and then climbed back up the mountain to say sorry to God and ask for two new stones.

'Until the people learn to obey me, they cannot go to their new home,' God said, sadly.

And so the Israelites wandered in the desert for many years, until they learned to trust God. Moses grew very old and died and a man, called Joshua, became the new leader of the Israelites.

Joshua blasts Jericho

When Joshua succeeded Moses as leader of the Israelites, his first job was to lead the people into Canaan, the country that God had promised would be their new home. But first there was just one small – or rather, big – problem: Jericho.

Jericho was a huge city, built like a castle. It had massive walls all the way around and it was very heavily-defended. 'Unless we can destroy it, we will never be safe from attack,' Joshua thought.

Joshua called all his military experts together. 'Before we can live in Canaan, we must destroy Jericho. I want you to make a plan,' he told them.

The next day, they returned – but no one had a plan. 'The walls are too thick and too tall – we'll never be able to knock them down,' they said. In those days, of course, tanks, bulldozers and dynamite had not been invented – so you can imagine how difficult it would be to destroy the walls. 'We can't do it!' they told Joshua.

Joshua did not know what to do, so he went off and prayed to God. 'Have you brought us all this way on a wild goose chase? You told us to go into this country to live. You told us to destroy Jericho but we can't. All my experts have tried their best but the walls are too strong. We can't do it!'

'True,' said God. '*You* can't do it – you're not strong enough. But I can. And I'll tell you how.'

The next day, Joshua assembled his men outside Jericho. When the people of Jericho saw them, they were alarmed. 'Quickly,' yelled the lookout. 'They're getting ready to attack!' But Joshua and his men did not attack. Instead, the trumpeters played and all the Israelites marched in total silence around the city – because that was what God had told Joshua to do.

At first, the people of Jericho were stunned into silence. Then, they burst out laughing. 'Your only weapon, a trumpet – too scared to attack? Are you trying to *bore* us to death?' they jeered.

But Joshua and the Israelites kept marching in silence. And they did this every day, for six days.

On the seventh day, again they did the same thing. They marched around the city walls in silence. Suddenly, they all shouted – the noise was deafening. The shouting grew louder and louder. It became more and more deafening. As they shouted, they heard the noise of cracking plaster and crumbling bricks and, all at once, the walls of Jericho came crashing down.

It was hard to tell which was the loudest – the walls crashing to the ground or Joshua and the Israelites cheering God's great victory. They had destroyed Jericho – God's way. Now it was safe, they could go into Canaan, their new home.

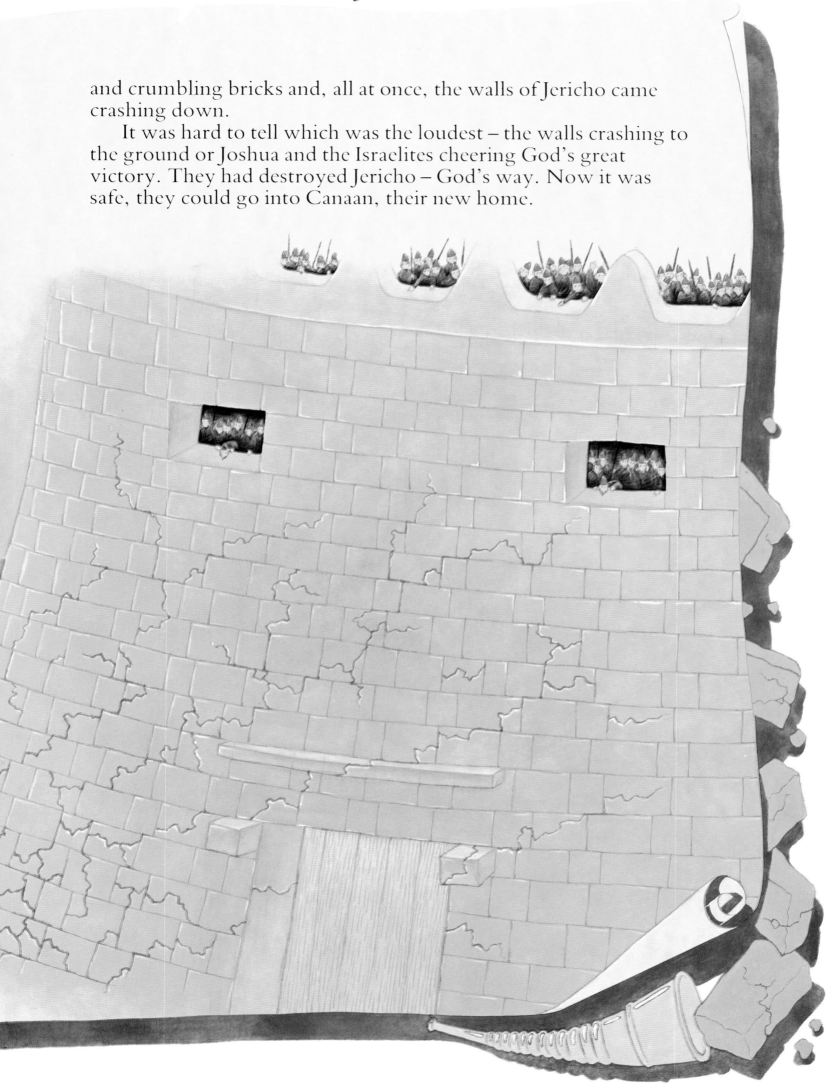

Jonah gets thrown in at the deep end

Once they had settled in the Promised Land, God wanted the Israelites to tell their neighbours about him. But not everyone was keen on this idea. Jonah was a prophet. It was his job to listen to God and then tell the people what God had said.

'Jonah,' God said one day, 'I want you to go to Nineveh.'

'Not that awful city,' moaned Jonah. 'It's full of evil people. They don't obey you at all.'

'That's the point. Tell them to stop being wicked or I'll destroy the city.'

'I don't want to go. They'll never listen to me. It's a long way. I get travel sick. Do I have to go?'

'It's an order,' said God.

So Jonah went to the port to catch a boat. But he didn't catch a boat to Nineveh – he caught one in the opposite direction. 'I'll get as far away from Nineveh as possible,' he thought. 'Somewhere God won't be able to find me.'

But God saw that Jonah had disobeyed him and decided to teach him a lesson. God made a huge storm. The boat was thrown backwards and forwards, tossed up and down on the huge waves. It got worse and worse. Jonah felt sick and the sailors were terrified out of their skins. They threw the cargo overboard to try to stop the boat sinking. But it made no difference and still the storm got worse.

'Perhaps God is angry with us,' a sailor suggested.

Jonah went pink. He felt so ashamed, he owned up. 'It's my fault. Throw me overboard and the storm will stop,' he cried.

The moment they threw him over the side, the storm stopped.

'Help!' thought Jonah. 'I can't swim.' But he didn't need to swim for, just at that very moment, God made a huge whale swim up to the surface. It swallowed Jonah in one gulp.

Poor Jonah found himself stuck inside the stomach of the whale. It was pitch dark, cold, wet and stank of fish. 'If only I'd done what God said. I'm such a fool. Going to Nineveh would never have been as bad as this. I'll never, ever disobey God again,' he thought.

Jonah was in the whale with nothing to eat for three days. On the third day, everything started to move. Jonah tried to stand up but he fell over. He was turned upside down and around and around. It must have felt just like being trapped in a washing machine. He felt terribly dizzy. 'Help!' he cried. Then he fainted.

The next thing he knew, he was lying on a beach. God had made the whale vomit and Jonah had been thrown up on to dry land – still stinking of fish.

'Well,' God said, 'are you ready to do what you're told?'

Jonah was, so he went to Nineveh, and straight to the King.

'If you don't stop being so wicked, God is going to destroy the city,' he told him. With that, Jonah retreated to a hillside nearby to watch the show. He loved fireworks and he thought it would be exciting to watch a whole city being blown up.

But the King and the people of Nineveh listened to what Jonah had said. They were sorry and realized how bad they had been. The King ordered everybody to obey God. When God saw that they were sorry, he decided not to destroy the city.

Jonah was furious. 'How could you let them off, after all the wicked things they've done? I've come all this way and now you're not going to destroy the city after all. I was hoping at least to see some fireworks!' And he went off into a big sulk.

'Jonah, you were just as bad – you disobeyed me. But I forgave you and rescued you from the whale,' God said, gently.

Jonah felt guilty. 'I'm sorry. Can I go home now?'

'Yes,' said God. 'And Jonah. Have a bath, you stink of fish!'

'Whose fault is that?' cried Jonah.

'Yours, for disobeying me,' said God.

And Jonah went off home to wash.

Gideon fights the Midianites

Jonah was not the only one who didn't like the job God had asked him to do. Things had not been going at all well for the Israelites and Gideon was feeling fed up. He was just wondering why God hadn't come to the rescue . . . when, suddenly, an angel appeared.

'God is with you, Gideon. He is on your side,' the angel said.

'Oh yes?' said Gideon, rather rudely forgetting that he was talking to an angel. 'Then why is everything going wrong? Life is a disaster at the moment. We're about to be invaded and wiped out by the Midianites!'

'That's what I've come about,' said the angel. 'You are going to rescue Israel from the Midianites.'

'Me?' he laughed. 'Very funny. Look at me – I'm the weakest in my family. You cannot be serious!'

But the angel was serious. God had chosen Gideon to fight the Midianites. Gideon, as you can imagine, was not thrilled by that. The Midianite army were fierce and there were thousands and thousands of them. In fact, they had so many camels it would take you a whole year to count them.

'Excuse me, sir, how do I know that this isn't some big joke? How do I know that this is really a message from God? What about giving me some proof? I'll tell you what. I'll put my sheepskin rug on the ground overnight and if, in the morning, there is dew on the rug but not on the ground, then I'll know that God really means he wants me to fight.'

'OK,' agreed the angel. 'Do it.' So he did . . . and, sure enough, in the morning, the sheepskin was damp but the ground was dry.

'Wow!' thought Gideon. But how could he be sure it was not just a fluke? So he asked the angel if he could double check. What about trying the test the other way around? This time, the ground must be wet and the rug dry. Sure enough, the next morning the ground was wet and the rug was dry.

'Bother!' thought Gideon. 'There's no getting out of it. It's ridiculous but God really does want me, of all people, to fight the Midianites,' and off he went to find some strong soldiers.

The next day, Gideon returned with a huge army, feeling very pleased with himself. But the angel was not quite so pleased . . .

'You've got too many men! You don't need a huge army when

42

you've got God on your side. Send anyone who is afraid home.'

'Does that mean I can go home?' asked Gideon. 'I'm terrified!'

'No,' said the angel. So Gideon had to stay and 22,000 men went home. That left Gideon with only 10,000 men.

'Right,' cried Gideon. 'Let's go and attack the Midianites!'

'No,' said the angel. 'You've still got too many men.'

This wasn't funny. 'I think I need a drink to cool down!' said Gideon and took the men down to the river to drink. Some men lay down, put their hands into the river and lapped up the water from their hands like dogs. Others went down on their knees to drink.

'Keep the men who lapped from their hands and send the others home,' the angel told Gideon.

'But that only leaves 300!' cried Gideon. 'It's not fair!' But Gideon had to send them away anyway.

So, with only 300 men, Gideon attacked the Midianites. They went in the middle of the night, using torches and making all sorts of frightening noises, shouting and blowing trumpets. The Midianites woke up and were so terrified they fled in panic.

Gideon and 300 men had won an extremely important battle. Or did God win it – and they just helped?

Samson's first haircut

God uses all sorts of people . . . some are argumentative, like Jonah . . . some are weak, like Gideon . . . and some are like Samson. Samson was no ordinary man. Before he was born, an angel told his mother to make sure he never cut his hair. His hair would give him superhuman strength to defeat Israel's enemy, the Philistines.

Sure enough, Samson grew to be the strongest man that ever lived. And, just as the angel had promised, he made a lot of trouble for his enemies, the Philistines. . . .

Samson fell in love with a Philistine girl and asked her to marry him. On the way to visit her one day, he came across a lion. He was not frightened – he just tore the lion in half with his bare hands. Walking home that evening, he saw honey bees had made a nest inside the dead lion. That got him thinking. Samson loved games especially brain-teasers. So, at his wedding feast, he set his enemies this riddle: 'Out of the eater came something to eat; out of the strong came something sweet.' The Philistines could not solve the riddle. So they cheated and made Samson's wife find out the answer.

Samson discovered they had cheated. He was furious. He caught 300 foxes, tied them together and set fire to their tails. The foxes ran through the fields, burning down the Philistines' crops. In revenge, the Philistines killed Samson's wife and then tried to kill Samson. But they could not capture him because he was so strong.

Some time later, Samson fell in love with a beautiful girl, called Delilah. The Philistines promised Delilah money if she could find out where Samson's strength came from. So, one morning, Delilah asked Samson the secret of his great strength.

'Tie me with seven new bowstrings and I'll be as weak as a normal man,' he said.

But, when she tried it, Samson

snapped the bowstrings. Delilah was cross, 'Tell me the truth.'

'Tie me up with new rope and I'll be as weak as anyone.'

But, when she tried it, Samson snapped the ropes.

Delilah was furious. She kept on nagging Samson until finally he told her where his strength lay.

That night, as Samson slept, Delilah cut off all his hair and, immediately, his strength left him.

The Philistines were then able to capture Samson easily. After cruelly blinding him, they took him to the palace to show him to the Philistine Kings.

Thousands of people gathered to laugh at Samson. Samson prayed one last prayer to God, 'Lord God, give me back my strength, just one more time. I am blind and ready to die. Give me revenge over the Philistines.' Then, he pushed with all his might against the pillars that held up the roof. His strength returned. The pillars groaned, cracked and crashed to the ground. The roof collapsed, killing everyone inside.

Samson died – but he killed more Philistines the day he died than in the whole of his life

put together.

Eli and Samuel

After Samson's victory, there was peace. But not all was well with the Israelites. Eli was a priest. He was very old and nearly blind. And he was very, very sad. He wondered if God had abandoned the Israelites. No one had had a vision or heard a message from God for years. Many people didn't believe in God anymore. Even Eli's family disobeyed God. 'At least Samuel believes in God,' thought Eli. Samuel was seven. He helped Eli and lived with him in the temple.

One night, when Eli was fast asleep, Samuel ran in. 'You called me,' Samuel said.

'No I didn't,' said Eli, 'go back to bed.' Eli nodded off and was gently snoring when Samuel burst into his room again.

'I know you called this time,' he said. 'What do you want?'

'I didn't call you.'

'But I know I wasn't dreaming,' said Samuel. 'I pinched myself to check and it hurt, so I know I was awake. You called my name.'

'I didn't call you,' replied Eli, 'I was fast asleep – like you ought to be. Go back to bed.' This time, Eli couldn't sleep. He tried to count sheep but it did not help. What if Samuel had not been dreaming? Perhaps he really had heard a voice. 'We'll wait and see if it happens again,' Eli thought.

Samuel ran in a third time. 'You definitely called me this time,' he cried.

Then, Eli understood what was going on. 'It wasn't me,' he said, 'it was God. Go back to bed. If God speaks again say, "Speak – your servant is listening," and listen carefully to what God says.' Eli did not get any more sleep that night. He lay awake, wondering what God wanted to say to the young boy.

As soon as morning came, Eli ran into Samuel's room. 'What did God say?' he asked.

'Promise you won't be cross with me?' replied Samuel.

'I won't be cross with you,' promised Eli. 'Tell me what God said.'

'God said that he is cross with your family. He said that your family are very disobedient so he is going to punish them,' said Samuel, sadly. 'I'm sorry,' whispered Samuel, 'I thought God would only say nice things.'

'No,' said Eli, 'God always speaks the truth. God tells us off when we don't obey him. But he only tells us off because he loves us and wants us to love Him too.'

Samuel still looked sad. 'Will God be angry with me and punish me?' he asked.

'Not if you listen to him and obey him. Come on, it's time for breakfast. I need lots of energy – I didn't get much sleep.'

David and Goliath

God often makes the strangest choices. When he wants a job done, he does not *usually* pick the strong macho type, like Samson. Instead, God does seem to pick the smallest, and weakest people. Take David, for example. David was the youngest boy, from the smallest family, in the smallest tribe, in the whole of Israel.

The Israelites were at war with their enemies, the Philistines. They had been at war for months and months. The Philistines were not much good at fighting but they had a special secret weapon – Goliath.

Goliath was a giant of a man. He was nearly nine foot tall. He wore bronze armour from head to toe and carried a huge bronze spear. You only had to look at him to feel faint with fear.

Each day, he came out and challenged the Israelites. 'Does anyone dare to fight me, man to man, in single combat?' But none of the Israelites was brave enough to fight him.

Saul, the King of the Israelites, was embarrassed. 'Isn't there anyone brave enough?' he asked his generals. There was a deathly hush.

David, who had been listening in a corner, spoke up, 'I'll go. I may only be a shepherd but I trust in God and, with God on your side, you don't need muscles or armour or anything – because God's the greatest!'

'Don't be ridiculous,' laughed one of the generals. 'You're only a small boy – Goliath's a giant and a trained soldier – he would have your guts for garters!'

'At least he's got some guts – unlike the rest of the army,' said the King. So Saul agreed to allow David to fight.

They dressed David up in a suit of armour. But the armour weighed so much, he could not move. 'I can't fight like this,' said David so he took it off and went just as he was.

When Goliath saw David, he fell about in hysterics. 'The only way you will kill me is if

I split my sides and die laughing!' he roared. 'Are you the best they can do? Are you their champion? How are you going to fight? You've got no armour or shield – look, you haven't even got a weapon!'

But Goliath was wrong. David had a catapult and five smooth stones. He loaded a stone, whirled the catapult around his head and let the stone fly. It struck Goliath right between the eyes with such force that it broke his skull, killing him instantly.

David ran forward, picked up Goliath's sword and cut off the giant's head.

The Philistines fled in panic; the Israelites cheered. God had defeated the Philistines – with one small boy and one small stone.

Elijah and the bonfire competition

David grew up to become King of all Israel – and he trusted God. Many years later, however, a new King came to the throne and he forgot all about God. . .
Elijah was feeling depressed. He was a prophet and it was his job to listen to God and tell people what God said. But no one seemed to believe in God any more. They worshipped the god, Baal, who was not real at all. Even the new King of Israel, Ahab, worshipped Baal. Worst of all, there were 450 phoney prophets who claimed that Baal was the greatest. He had been arguing with them all morning. 'Baal is just a load of rubbish,' argued Elijah.

'Baal's the greatest,' they all cried.

'Don't be stupid. God is the greatest.' Tempers were getting frayed. Elijah knew that, any minute, they might come to blows. Then he had a brainwave. 'We'll have a competition to settle this,' he said. 'You kill a bull and offer it as a sacrifice to Baal. I'll offer a sacrifice to God. Each of us must build a bonfire and put the bull on the top. But we won't light it. Instead, you pray to Baal and I'll pray to God. If your prayers are answered and Baal lights your bonfire, then I'll worship him. But, if God lights my bonfire, we'll know God is the greatest.' Everyone agreed and the prophets of Baal went first. They built a bonfire and started to pray. They prayed for an hour. Nothing happened. Elijah began to tease

them. 'Perhaps Baal's day-dreaming,' he laughed. 'Perhaps he's fallen asleep. Pray louder – you might wake him up!' The prophets of Baal scowled but they went on praying. Nothing happened. 'Perhaps he's gone somewhere,' laughed Elijah. 'Or maybe he's deaf. Pray louder and he might be able to hear you!' Their prayers grew louder and louder, until they were shouting. They prayed for hours but nothing happened. Finally, they collapsed, exhausted. 'Have you finished?' smiled Elijah. 'I can't see much smoke or fire for that matter. Perhaps it's Baal's day off.'

Now it was Elijah's turn to prepare his sacrifice. He built an altar with stone, added wood and laid the bull on top. Then he poured 12 buckets of water over the bonfire.

One of the Prophets of Baal laughed. 'There's no need to try and put it out with water, you haven't got it lit yet!'

Then Elijah prayed – just one short prayer. 'Lord God, answer my prayer and prove that you are the only God.'

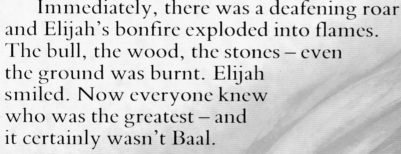

Immediately, there was a deafening roar and Elijah's bonfire exploded into flames. The bull, the wood, the stones – even the ground was burnt. Elijah smiled. Now everyone knew who was the greatest – and it certainly wasn't Baal.

The fiery furnace

Even after Elijah proved that God was the greatest, the King of Israel still ignored God. So God let the King of Israel be defeated by the King of Babylon. Now, Nebuchadnezzar was King of Babylon. He had a big empire. And he had a very big head. He thought he was the greatest man that had ever lived. In fact, he thought he was the greatest – full stop! He had such a high opinion of himself that he had a statue made. It was taller than most people's houses and made of solid gold. He issued an order saying that everyone must worship his statue. Whenever the palace band started to play, everyone had to stop whatever they were doing and bow down to his statue.

The first morning the band struck up and King Nebuchadnezzar went on to the balcony of the palace to watch. Right across the square, all he could see were people's backs as they knelt down and worshipped the statue. Except in one corner. Down to his left, there were three men and they were all standing up. Nebuchadnezzar stormed out of the palace and across the square.

'Who are you and what do you think you are doing?'

'Er, I'm Shadrach, this is Meshach and he's Abednego, your majesty. And we're not doing anything. We're just standing here.'

'I gave an order that everyone must bow down and worship my statue. So get on with it!' The three men did not move. King Nebuchadnezzar went red. 'Did you hear me?' he screamed.

'Er, yes, your majesty. But we're from Israel. We worship God and nobody else. So we can't bow down to your statue.'

Nebuchadnezzar went purple. 'I'll give you one last chance. If you don't bow down, I'll throw you into the fiery furnace.'

The fiery furnace was a huge oven, big enough to throw people into. Shadrach, Meshach and Abednego shivered. But they did not bow down. Nebuchadnezzar went white with rage, 'Take them away!' The guards marched them off and threw them into the fiery furnace. It was so hot that one guard had his moustache burnt off.

'That's the end of them,' smirked Nebuchadnezzar. But, when he looked again, his eyes nearly popped out of his head. Not only were they not being burnt at all – but, there, in the middle of the flames, were *four* people walking about. 'Quick, get them out!' stammered the King. Out came Shadrach, Meshach and Abednego. They were not burnt; they did not even smell of smoke.

'Where's the fourth man?'

'That wasn't a man. That was God. God promised that whatever happens to us, wherever we go, he will always be with us. And he's never let us down.'

Nebuchadnezzar suddenly felt very small. He had his statue melted down and gave a new order. Everyone was to worship God. For God was the greatest – not Nebuchadnezzar.

Daniel in the lions' den

Daniel had had an up-and-down sort of life. He'd been captured by the King of Babylon and thrown into prison. Twice he'd almost been executed. But, whether things were going well or badly, Daniel always trusted God and prayed to Him every day.

Some years after Nebuchadnezzar had died, Darius became King of Babylon. Once, the King threatened to kill all his advisers unless they could tell him what he had dreamt the previous night. His magicians and advisers failed and the executioner was sharpening his axe, when Daniel heard about it. Daniel told the King what he had dreamt and what it meant. The King was so impressed, he took Daniel out of prison and made him governor. The magicians and advisers were very jealous. They thought Daniel was a bit of a show off. However, they did not dare be rude to him because he was the King's favourite.

One day, however, they thought up a plan of how to get rid of Daniel. The King had one weakness – he was very proud and easily flattered. They went to the King and really grovelled. 'Oh King, may you live for ever. You are the greatest. There is no one as wonderful as you!' The King's head began to swell. 'We have a suggestion to make. Issue an order that nobody in the kingdom is to pray for a month, unless they pray to you. If they disobey, have

them thrown into the lions' den.' King Darius liked that. He signed and sealed the order. Although Daniel saw the order, he still prayed to God.

The next day, the advisers came to the King. 'Your majesty, someone has broken the order you signed yesterday.'

'Very well,' said the King. 'Throw him to the lions. By the way, who is it?'

When the King heard that it was Daniel, he realized he had been tricked. But he was powerless. Once a law had been sealed, even the King could not change it.

'I'm sorry,' the King said to Daniel, 'I've made a terrible mistake. May your God protect you.' And, reluctantly, he gave the order for Daniel to be thrown to the lions.

The King hardly slept a wink all night. Every time he dropped off, he had nightmares of lions with huge white teeth. In the morning, he rushed out of his room, still wearing his pyjamas and went straight to the lions' den. 'Daniel! . . . Daniel! Talk to me – are you still alive? Did God look after you?'

'I'm fine,' laughed Daniel. 'I slept like a log – so did the lions.'

The king was overjoyed. He took Daniel out of the pit. All the men who had plotted against Daniel were thrown to the lions. The lions were now wide awake and gobbled them up, bones and all.

Jesus 'the Rescuer' is born

God had promised Adam that, one day, he would send someone very special to rescue people from the powers of evil and from death. The Israelites waited and waited for their promised rescuer, whom they called the Messiah. They thought God would send a powerful warrior King to free them from their enemies. But God had a different plan. God sent Jesus. Jesus was 'the Rescuer' and this is the story of his birth.

Mary was an ordinary girl – though what happened to her is the most extraordinary story in the world. One day, Mary was hanging out the washing. She bent down and, when she stood up, she nearly fainted. There, in front of her, was an angel.

'Don't be afraid,' the angel said. 'I'm Gabriel.' Mary thought she must be dreaming. She pinched herself to check – 'ouch,' no she was certainly awake. 'I have a message from God,' the angel said. 'You are going to have a baby – but not just any baby. Your baby will be special, the most special baby ever.'

'I'm sorry,' said Mary, 'I do believe you – but I just don't understand. How can I have a baby when I'm not married?'

'He is God's special child,' the angel explained, 'put there in a special way by God's Holy Spirit. He won't have a human father. God will be his father. And you must call him Jesus, which means "the Rescuer", because he will rescue the world from evil and death.'

'What will Joseph think?' said Mary. 'I love him very much and we are engaged to be married. He'll never believe me!'

'Leave that to me,' said the angel. And the angel went off and explained it all to Joseph.

So Mary and Joseph got married. Several months later, they returned to their home town, Bethlehem, for a survey as the

Romans, who ruled the country, wanted to count everybody. When they arrived in Bethlehem, it was terribly crowded. All the hotels and inns were full. At each place, the answer was the same, 'Sorry – no room.' 'Isn't there anywhere?' begged Joseph. 'My wife is about to have a baby.'

'No. We've only got a stable at the back. It's dry but you'll have to share it with the animals.'

So, there, in a stable behind a pub in Bethlehem, the most special baby was born. They gave him the name the angel had said – Jesus. Mary put the baby into one of the mangers, used for feeding the cattle; it made the perfect cot. She lay down to get some sleep, it had been a long night. But the excitement was not over yet.

Mary and Joseph have some visitors

Mary had just closed her eyes and was counting sheep to get herself to sleep, when Joseph woke her up. 'Mary,' whispered Joseph. 'There are some men outside. They have come to see the baby.'

'How do they know about the baby?' she asked, sleepily.

'An angel told them.'

The shepherds trooped in, very shy and embarrassed and stared at the baby. 'We saw these angels,' they said. 'They were singing about a baby King. We couldn't believe our eyes, so we came to see for ourselves. Odd sort of place for a King to be born but he must be special – those angels said so. Anyway, you must get plenty of rest.' And off they went, back to their flocks of sheep.

'Now I can get some sleep,' thought Mary.

Some days later, Joseph came in and spoke to Mary.

'Er, Mary? There are some more men outside. They've come to see the baby.'

'Well, tell them to come back in the morning. I'm tired.'

'Er, Mary, they are, er, Kings – Kings, from the Far East. They've come all this way to see the baby.'

'How do they know about him? I suppose that angel told them.'

'No,' said Joseph. 'They followed a star.'

The three Kings came in and explained. 'We followed this star – we've never seen anything like it before. We knew that it must mean a King had been born. We went to the palace – after all, that's where you'd expect a King to be born. At first, King Herod

seemed angry but then he was very nice. We promised to let him know where the baby is, so he can come and see him.'

The Kings gave Mary and Joseph gifts they had brought for Jesus. Gifts fit for a King: gold, frankincense and myrrh. Then they slept in the courtyard and, once more, Mary tried to get some sleep. But no one was to get much sleep that night.

As they slept, the Kings had a dream. It warned them not to tell King Herod where the baby was. So they left quietly, long before morning and went straight home, without telling Herod.

Mary was just getting back to sleep, when Joseph woke her.

'What is it now?' she asked. 'More people?'

'No,' said Joseph. 'I saw that angel again. He said we must leave immediately and take the baby to Egypt. It isn't safe to stay here. King Herod wants to kill the baby.'

So, just before dawn, Joseph and Mary left the stable and set out for Egypt. It was a night they would never forget. And a night when Mary got no sleep at all.

John the Baptist is born

Meanwhile, back in Jerusalem, at about the same time, there were other strange things happening – and they, too, surrounded the birth of another baby boy. . .
Zechariah was a priest who worked in the temple in Jerusalem. It was his job to help at the special services. One day, everyone was gathered in the main part of the temple as usual, waiting for the service to start. Zechariah went through the curtain into the holy of holies, the place where only the priests were allowed to go. The service began and Zechariah was in the middle of his prayers when, suddenly, God spoke to him, 'Zechariah, your wife, Elizabeth, is going to have a baby.'

His name is John

'That's ridiculous,' said Zechariah, 'my wife is far too old to have children. You must have made a mistake.'

'Listen,' said God, 'there's no mistake. Nothing is impossible for me.'

'But my wife, Elizabeth, is far too old to have children,' said Zechariah.

'Don't you know your history?' said God. 'Abraham was 100 years old and his wife Sarah 90 when they had their son, Isaac. Nothing is impossible for me.'

'That sort of thing only happens in stories . . . long, long ago,' said Zechariah. 'It couldn't happen today. And, even if it did, nothing like that would ever happen to me.'

'You do talk nonsense,' said God. 'If I promise something will happen, then it always does. I'll prove it to you. To stop you arguing and talking any more nonsense, I'm going to make you dumb. You won't be able to speak until after your son is born. And, when he is, you must call him John.'

All this took quite a long time, especially with Zechariah arguing so much. The people waiting in the temple began to wonder what was happening . . . they did not want to be late home for tea. At last, Zechariah came out, looking white.

'What took you so long? . . . what happened?' they asked. But Zechariah could not tell them . . . he could not say a word. And he did not say a word for nine months!

Eventually, Elizabeth had a son.

'What is his name?' her friends asked. When she told them it was John, they were surprised. You see, it was the custom in Israel to name a child after someone in the family. 'But there's no one else in your family called "John" – are you sure that's the right name?' they asked.

So they checked with Zechariah. But Zechariah still could not speak, so he wrote the name out instead. 'His name is John,' he wrote.

They were all very surprised. But they were even more surprised when Zechariah suddenly started to talk again.

'Tell us what happened,' they said. 'Start right at the beginning.'

So Zechariah sat them down and began to tell them the strange story of the birth of his son.

Jesus is baptized by John

When John grew up, he became a hermit. He lived in the desert and ate locusts and wild honey. He never shaved or cut his hair and wore camel-skins instead of clothes. Meanwhile Mary, Joseph and Jesus had moved back from Egypt to their home town, Nazareth, because King Herod had died. Joseph worked as a carpenter and Jesus helped him. But Jesus was not to remain a carpenter. There was more important work for him to do. Jesus' work began the day he was baptized by John.

One day, God told John to leave the desert. 'I want you to baptize people in the River Jordan. They must say sorry for all the things they've done wrong. They must be washed in the river, to show that I will wash away all their sins. Very soon, I am going to send the Messiah to rescue people from the power of evil. One day, you'll see my Holy Spirit come down from heaven like a dove and land on a man. You will know that he is the Messiah, the Rescuer.'

People came from miles around to be baptized by John. One morning, Jesus came down to the river and joined the queue of people waiting to be baptized. When it came to his turn, Jesus stepped forward and John baptized him. Just as Jesus stepped out of the water, the clouds parted and a bright beam of light shone down on him. John looked up in amazement. In the beam of light, a dove was hovering, just above Jesus' head. A voice broke the silence, 'This is my son. I am very pleased with him.'

John knew it was God's voice. It had all happened just as God had told him. John stared at Jesus. This was the man God had sent

to rescue the world from evil and death. John was still
staring, when Jesus said, 'I must go now. I have work
to do.'
Jesus decided he would pick a team to help him.
He chose 12 men who were called his disciples, or
followers. They were a mixed sort of bunch.
He chose a tax-collector, called Matthew.
'Leave what you're doing and follow me.
I've got more important work for you
to do,' he told him. Immediately,
Matthew left his work and
followed Jesus. Another time,
Jesus told some fishermen to
follow him and that is the
next story.

James and John go fishing

James and John were fishermen. Their father owned a fish shop in Jerusalem, with a big sign outside saying, 'Zebedee and Sons – Fishmongers; By appointment to King Herod.' One night, the two brothers were fishing on Lake Galilee. Their friend, Peter, was in his boat nearby. 'We'll race you to see who can catch the most,' they yelled across to him.

So they threw their nets out and watched them sink into the water. After waiting an hour, they pulled them in. They could not believe their eyes – not a single fish. They threw the nets out again and waited another hour. 'This time, there'll be plenty,' said James. But, when they pulled them in, they were empty.

So they threw the nets out a third time and waited. Again, they pulled them in. Still nothing. They had never known a night like it.

'I haven't caught a thing,' yelled Peter.

'Neither have we,' they replied. 'We'll be here all night.'

Again, they threw their nets out. It started to rain. 'I'm cold and miserable,' moaned John. 'Let's go home.'

'We can't go home empty-handed,' said James. 'What would Dad say? And Peter would laugh at us!' So they carried on. They fished all night but did not catch a thing. At sunrise, they headed for home, thoroughly fed up.

Just as they got to the shore, they saw Jesus. 'Catch anything?' he asked. 'I could do with a bite to eat for breakfast.'

'Sorry,' said James, 'We didn't catch a thing.'

'Try throwing your nets out on the other side,' said Jesus.

'What difference can that make?' thought John, sulkily. 'Anyway, what does he know about fishing? – he's a carpenter.' But they did what Jesus said anyway. Back they went and threw their nets overboard again. 'It'll never work,' said John.

'Pull them in,' yelled Jesus.

'Give the fish a chance to swim into them!' cried James.

'Pull them in,' Jesus insisted. So they did – or at least they tried to. James gave a great big tug and nearly fell overboard. John grabbed him by the ankles and pulled. But the net was so full of fish, they could not lift it on board – in fact, it was pulling the whole boat down. Finally, they managed to drag the net ashore.

'Looks like we work well together!' said Jesus. 'I'd like you to join my team.'

'That's fine by me!' said Peter and they all agreed.

'Good,' said Jesus. 'But first – let's have breakfast – there's plenty here!'

In fact, there was more than enough for second helpings.

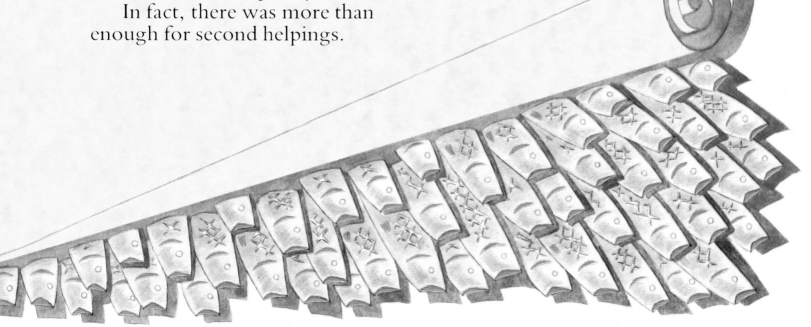

The lost son

Jesus told his disciples that God is like a father. He taught them the prayer which begins, 'Our Father, who art in Heaven'. To help people understand how much God the Father loves us, Jesus told them this story.

'There was a man who had two sons. The younger son was fed up with living at home. He was impatient and greedy. However much he had, he always wanted more. So he went to his father and said, "Dad, you know the money I'll inherit when you die? Can I have it now?"

'The father was hurt – it sounded like his son could not wait for him to die. But he gave his son the money.

'So the son left home and went to live in a big hotel in the city. He bought expensive clothes, gold jewellery and went camel-racing. At night, he gambled. Very quickly, he spent all his money. "I must get a job," he said. But there were no jobs at the job centre. After having nothing to eat for three days, he finally found a job with a farmer, feeding pigs. He was so hungry, he even tried eating some of the pigs' food. "Euch! It's disgusting!" he cried out loud.

'"You're supposed to feed the pigs!" shouted the farmer, who had seen him. "Not steal their food. You're fired!"

'The son sat in the gutter – his stomach rumbled. A tear rolled down his cheek and he began to cry. He was very hungry and very lonely. All at once, he had a brainwave. "I'll go home and say sorry. I'll ask Dad if he'll take me back as a servant."

'He knew people would laugh at him and call him a fool but he was too hungry to care. So he set off. His clothes were in rags and he had not washed for a month. He wondered what his father would say. He was sure to be furious. But, as he approached the village, he got the shock of his life.

'His father saw him in the distance and ran to meet him. He threw his arms around the boy, "Welcome home, son," he said and tears filled his eyes.

' "Dad, I'm sorry I treated you so badly. I don't deserve to be your son."

' "I love you," said the father. "You'll always be welcome at home. Now you'd better go and get ready for the party."

' "What party?" asked the son.

' "The party to celebrate your return," the father said. "Now hurry up and get changed."

'A tear rolled down the son's cheek. He had not realized just how much his father loved him. It was good to be home.'

Jesus feeds the crowd

David rushed up to his mum. 'Mum, can I go and see Jesus? Everybody else is going, please can I go too?'

'As long as you take something to eat with you,' she said and packed him a picnic of five small loaves and two small fish.

David ran off. He'd heard so much about Jesus and couldn't wait to see him for himself.

That day, Jesus told stories, beautiful stories about God. The crowd listened quietly. David loved the stories. No one noticed the time go by and it was nearly evening when Jesus finished.

'It's getting late,' said Andrew, one of Jesus' disciples. 'It's time everybody went home for supper. They must be starving.'

'Then give them something to eat,' said Jesus.

'Where are we supposed to get anything to eat? The nearest shop must be miles away. And, even if the shops were open, how would we pay for it? It would take a year's wages to buy enough food for this lot.'

'I didn't say anything about buying food. I just said feed them,' replied Jesus, gently.

'With what?' asked Andrew, grumpily. 'Nobody's brought any sandwiches.'

Just then, David, who'd been sitting near the front, spoke up. 'Excuse me, I've got five loaves and two fish. I don't mind sharing.'

'How far do you think five loaves and two fish will go? There must be 5000 people here!' snapped Andrew, rudely.

The little boy looked sad, 'It's all I've got.'

Jesus just looked at David and smiled. 'Thank you,' he said. 'That'll do nicely.'

The boy smiled back. Jesus seemed nicer than the others.

Jesus took the loaves of bread and the fish and said a prayer of thanks to God.

'Pass it around,' he told his disciples.

'This won't take long,' mumbled Andrew.

But it did. They passed the five loaves and two fish along the first row, then back down the second. The more people took, the more there seemed to be! The baskets with the fish and bread went around everybody – but they never ran out. Everybody had plenty to eat and there was even enough for seconds. 'I'm sorry,' Andrew said. 'I didn't think we could feed them all.'

'With God's help, you can do anything,' said Jesus. 'All that God asks is that you give him what you have. He'll do the rest.'

'Can we go home now?' asked Andrew.

'Haven't you forgotten something?' laughed Jesus. 'What about the clearing up?'

The disciples tidied up and the strangest thing was – there were more scraps left over than when they'd started – 12 basketfuls.

David went home happy. He had quite a story to tell his mum, about the man who fed over 5000 people using a packed lunch – his packed lunch! 'Will she believe me?' he thought.

Zacchaeus finds a friend

Zacchaeus,
the tax–collector,
was not a popular man. He did not have a single
friend. Tax collectors, rather like traffic wardens,
find it difficult to make friends. Also, no one liked
him because he cheated people to become rich.

Zacchaeus lived in a luxury house in Jericho. One day,
he heard that Jesus was visiting the town. He had heard
about the wonderful things Jesus did. So, he took the day off
work and went to see Jesus for himself. Everyone else had taken
the day off too. There was a huge crowd and Zacchaeus was not
very tall. In fact, he was only four foot four and he couldn't see
above all the people. First, he tried shoving his way through the
crowd. 'Who's pushing?' they cried, angrily, and pushed him
straight to the back. Zacchaeus was about to give up, when he saw
a tree. He had to jump to get hold of the bottom branch but,

finally, he climbed into it. What a good view, right over the crowd. He could see Jesus . . . and Jesus could see him.

'Hello, Zacchaeus,' called Jesus. 'You'd better climb down from that tree. I'm coming to your home for dinner!'

Zacchaeus did not have to climb down. He fell right out of the tree with shock and ran home to prepare food. He put a brand new table-cloth on the table and got out his best dishes made of gold. They hadn't been used because no one had ever come to visit.

Jesus and Zacchaeus ate together. Zacchaeus was on his fourth piece of bread, when Jesus asked him, gently, 'Zacchaeus, you're a thief aren't you?' Zacchaeus choked on his bread. 'These dishes don't really belong to you, do they?'

Zacchaeus spilt his drink, 'Yes, I am a thief,' he said.

'What are you going to do about it?' asked Jesus, kindly.

'I . . . I . . . I'd better give the money back. I'll give it all back. In fact, I'll give back more than I stole.'

Jesus smiled, 'I'm glad I came to dinner.'

'So am I,' said Zacchaeus.

It had cost him a lot of money but he had found a friend.

The blind man

Jesus stayed that night at Zacchaeus the tax-collector's house, in Jericho. The next morning, he set off with his disciples.

Now, there was a blind man, called Bartimaeus, who lived in Jericho and every day he begged at the side of the road. When he heard that Jesus was passing, he began to shout, 'Jesus! Jesus! Have pity on me!'

The people standing around were embarrassed and told Bartimaeus to shut up but he just shouted even louder and thumped his begging bowl on the ground to make as much noise as possible.

'Jesus!' he yelled. 'Spare a thought for a blind man.'

As Jesus approached, he heard the noise and asked his disciples to fetch the man.

'It's your lucky day,' they told Bartimaeus. 'He's calling you over.'

Bartimaeus leapt to his feet and rushed over to Jesus.

'What do you want me to do for you?' Jesus asked, gently.

'I want to be able to see again,' he said. 'I know you can give me back my sight.'

Jesus looked at him and smiled. 'Your faith has made you well.'

Instantly, Bartimaeus could see again. He leapt up and down. He couldn't believe his eyes! 'No more begging for me,' he cried and followed Jesus down the road, doing cartwheels all the way.

Jesus healed many people like Bartimaeus on his travels. He cured blind people, deaf people, lame people and people who suffered from leprosy. One time, a man came to Jesus who was deaf and dumb. Jesus put his fingers in the man's ears.

'I hope his ears are clean!' whispered one of the disciples.

Then, Jesus spat on his hand and touched the man's tongue.

'Euch,' said Peter, under his breath. 'How revolting.'

Jesus looked at the man and said just two

words, 'Open up.' Immediately, the man's ears were healed and he could hear. He opened his mouth. He could talk perfectly normally.

'I don't know about sticking fingers in ears and then spitting on tongues,' laughed Peter. 'But it certainly works!'

Jesus brings the roof down

Jesus' reputation spread like wild fire. Wherever he went, people thronged to see him. They came to hear the stories he told; they came to him to be healed. They had never known anyone like him before. He only had to touch them and they got better. He would say a couple of words and lepers were healed, cripples could walk, blind men could see. News spread fast and soon thousands of people were bringing sick friends for Jesus to heal.

Ben had been a cripple for years. He could not walk and had been confined to his house, unable to go outside, for a long time. One day, four friends rushed in.

'We are going to Capernaum,' they said.

'Have a nice time,' said Ben.

'No, we're *all* going. You're coming, too.'

'But it's miles and I can't walk, remember?'

'We know. We'll carry you on a stretcher. We're taking you to Jesus – he can heal you.'

So they set off. They took it in turns, carrying Ben, two at a time. He was very heavy and it was hot. They huffed and puffed. 'I wish you'd gone on a diet,' one of them said. 'You weigh a ton.'

'Actually, I weigh ten and a half stone,' said Ben, quite offended.

Finally, they reached Capernaum – but thousands of other people had got there before them. They could not see Jesus at all but it was easy to see which house he was in – it was completely surrounded by people.

The four friends tried to push their way through with the stretcher.

'Make way!' they yelled. 'We have a sick man.'

'So have we,' the crowd yelled back.

'We'll never make it,' said Ben. 'Let's go back home.'

Then one of them had a brainwave. They went around to the back of the house. 'We'll never get in this way,' said Ben.

'Oh yes we will!' they cried and climbed up on to the roof, taking Ben, still on the stretcher, with them. They started to dismantle the roof until, at last, they had made a hole in the ceiling. You can imagine the shock on the faces of the people in the room below. Jesus looked up and smiled. They lowered Ben through.

'Stand up and walk,' said Jesus. 'You can carry your stretcher home yourself.'

'Phew,' cried his four friends. 'We couldn't have carried it another step, and certainly not all the way home again.'

But Ben did not walk home. He half ran, half skipped – he was so thrilled to be able to use his legs.

And he carried his stretcher, all the way!

Jesus heals a young girl

One day, an important Jewish official, called Jairus, came to Jesus. He threw himself at Jesus' feet, 'My little girl is very sick. If you hurry and come straight away, I know you can make her well.'

Jesus and his disciples set off immediately. It was slow going because there was a huge crowd and everyone was trying to see Jesus. They pushed their way through the crowd with Jairus leading the way.

Suddenly, Jesus stopped. 'Someone touched me,' he said.

'Don't be daft,' said Peter. 'In a crowd like this, of course someone touched you.'

'No,' said Jesus. 'Someone touched me. I felt power go out of me. Who touched my clothes?'

Jairus was getting frantic.

'Please hurry or it'll be too late and my daughter will die.'

But Jesus insisted on finding out who had touched him. 'Who touched my clothes?' he asked again. Everyone was silent.

'I did,' came a quiet voice from the crowd. A woman stepped forward. 'I touched your coat because I thought, if I touched your clothes, I would get better.'

'Well?' asked Jesus, kindly. 'Did touching my clothes work?'

'Yes,' she said.

'Then you can go,' he smiled. 'Your faith has made you well.'

Just then, some of the servants arrived from Jairus' house.

'It's too late,' they cried, 'your daughter is dead.'

Jairus burst into tears. 'If only we hadn't stopped.'

Jesus looked at him. 'Don't cry,' he said, gently. 'Trust me.'

They made their way to Jairus' house. In the courtyard, they found everyone crying. 'Why are you making all this fuss?' Jesus asked. 'The child isn't dead, she's just fast asleep.'

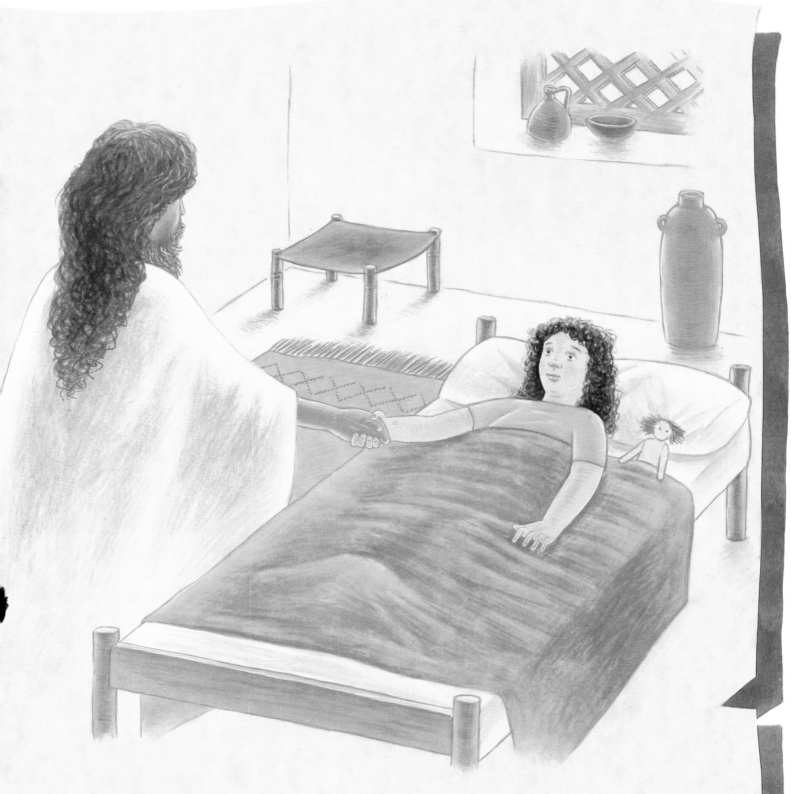

    Jesus went up to the
girl's room and, gently, took her
by the hand. 'It's time to get up,' he said.
She immediately climbed out of bed and they walked
down into the courtyard together. No one could believe their eyes.
They stared first at the girl, then at Jesus, then at the girl again.
    Jesus smiled at the little girl. 'Time for something to eat. You
must be starving!'

The disciples nearly capsize

One evening, Jesus and his disciples decided to go to the village of Gerasa, on the other side of Lake Galilee, to get something to eat. 'Let's go there by boat, it'll be much quicker,' suggested Peter.

'Do we have to?' moaned Matthew. 'I'm not very good on water. I get seasick.'

'Don't be daft, you'll be fine!' said Peter, confidently. 'There's nothing to worry about.' But Peter was soon to be proved wrong.

They climbed aboard Peter's boat and set off, with Peter at the helm. Jesus was tired. He'd been teaching and telling the crowds stories all day so he went to the back of the boat to lie down. And he fell fast asleep.

Meanwhile, as Peter steered, the others talked about the extraordinary things that had happened since they had been with Jesus. They talked about the miracles he had done. The time he fed 5000 people. The time he healed Bartimaeus. They laughed about the man who had been lowered through the roof. They all agreed that Jesus was the most amazing person they had ever met. They were so busy talking, they did not notice the change in the weather. At first it began to drizzle and then the wind began to pick up.

There were often storms on Lake Galilee. Peter, Andrew, James and John had all been fishermen before they had become Jesus' disciples. They had fished on Lake Galilee many times and they had been out in dozens of storms. The boat pitched back and forth and side to side. One or two of the disciples began to feel seasick. 'Don't worry,' said Peter, 'It'll soon pass.'

But it didn't. It got worse and worse. Waves crashed over the side of the boat.

'I can't swim!' cried Matthew.

And still it got worse. Even Peter was worried now. He'd never been in a storm like this before and they were still a long way from the shore.

'We're all going to drown,' panicked Matthew. 'Quick! We must wake Jesus up.' Matthew went to the back of the boat. 'How can you sleep through this?' he cried, waking Jesus up. 'Don't you care if we drown? Can't you do something?'

'Matthew, don't you trust me after all we've been through?' asked Jesus, gently.

Jesus stood up. He looked up at the clouds. 'Be still!' he said. He looked at the sea. 'Be quiet!' he commanded. Instantly, the sky cleared and the rain stopped. The sea became calm and the sun came out.

The disciples stared at Jesus with open mouths. They knew he must be special. Even the wind and waves obeyed him. Soon, they reached the far shore and climbed out on to dry land.

'That's the last time I go for a joy ride,' said Matthew. 'Next time, I think I'll walk round!'

Jesus rides into Jerusalem

One day, Jesus called his disciples together. 'We must go to Jerusalem,' he told them. 'James and John, you go to the village. You'll find a donkey there. Untie it and bring it to me.'

'What if someone thinks we're stealing it?' they asked.

'Just tell them I need it,' said Jesus.

They found the donkey, just as Jesus had said. They were untying it, when a man stopped them. 'Hey – what are you doing with my donkey?' When they explained that Jesus needed it, he let them go.

As they brought the donkey back, they realized why Jesus wanted it. A prophet had said that the Messiah, 'the Rescuer', would enter Jerusalem, riding on a donkey.

And so, Jesus and his disciples set off to Jerusalem, with Jesus riding on a donkey. People came out of their houses and lined the roadside. They loved Jesus and began to cheer. They knew he was special. 'Hosanna! Hurrah for the King, who comes in the name of God. Hurrah!' they shouted. They spread clothes, coats and cloaks on the ground to make a carpet as he rode along. When they ran out of cloaks, they cut branches from the palm trees and threw them on the ground in front of Jesus. The branches made a bright green carpet all the way to Jerusalem.

The crowd grew
bigger and the cheering
louder. They had been
waiting for the Messiah,
the Rescuer, for so long. At
last, the waiting was over. Now
Jesus had come, things would be
different. 'He'll be crowned King,' they
said to one another, 'and then all our
troubles will be over.' They loved Jesus and
thought he would make a wonderful King.

But not everyone was pleased to see Jesus. The
chief priests hated Jesus. They were jealous because he
was so popular.

When Jesus arrived in Jerusalem, he rode straight to the
temple. Inside the temple, people were selling animals for the
sacrifices. Money-changers were busy counting out their money.

Jesus grabbed a rope and chased them all out of the temple. He
kicked over their tables and coins flew everywhere. The disciples
had never seen Jesus angry like this before.

'This temple is supposed to be a place where people pray to
God,' he cried. 'These crooks have made it more like a
marketplace!'

The priests and money-changers were furious. 'I told you he
was a trouble-maker,' one of them said. 'Arrest him for causing a
breach of the peace!'

But they did not dare to arrest Jesus because the crowd were on
his side. Instead, they began to plan how to get rid of him.

The Last Supper

Every year, people came to Jerusalem to celebrate the Passover. At Passover, they remembered the time God rescued the Israelites from Egypt.

As Passover approached, Jesus called his disciples together. 'You must make the arrangements for the Passover. Go to the town. You'll see a man carrying water on his head. Ask him if we can use the upstairs room in his house.'

The disciples did as Jesus said and, on the Thursday evening, Passover night, they all met together in the upper room.

Jesus stood up to talk to them. 'Many years ago, God rescued your great-great-grandparents, the Israelites, from Egypt. We eat this meal to remind us of that rescue, when he protected them from the angel of death. The time has come for a new rescue. This time, a different lamb will be killed to rescue you from death. I am that lamb. I have come to Jerusalem to be killed, so that everyone can be free from the power of evil and death.'

Jesus picked up the bread. 'This bread reminds you how the women left in such a hurry they didn't have time to finish baking. Tonight, I give it a new meaning. From now on, it will remind you of my body, which will be broken on a cross for you.' He passed the bread around and the disciples ate some.

He picked up the cup of wine. 'This wine reminds you of the blood your ancestors painted on the doorposts, to protect them from the angel of death. From now on, it will remind you of my blood, which will be shed to protect you from death.' He passed around the cup of wine and all the disciples drank some.

'Tomorrow, I will be arrested and put on trial. They will crucify me on a cross. But do not worry. That is not the end.'

The disciples could not take it all in. 'They'll never arrest you,' said Peter. 'We'll defend you!'

Jesus looked at him. 'One of you will betray me,' he said. 'And you, Peter, you will deny you even *knew* me.'

'Never!' cried Peter.

'I tell you the truth,' said Jesus, 'before the cock crows, you'll say you don't know me three times.'

'Is one of us really going to betray you?' asked John.

'One of you is going to hand me over to the chief priests. He will lead the temple police to me and help them arrest me.'

As Jesus spoke, Judas slipped quietly out of the room and headed for the chief priest's house. The chief priest had offered Judas 30 pieces of silver to lead the temple guards to Jesus.

Jesus and the other disciples finished the meal. Then they left the upper room and walked to the Garden of Gethsemane.

Jesus is arrested

It was dark when Jesus and his disciples reached the Garden of Gethsemane. The garden on the hillside overlooking Jerusalem was one of Jesus' favourite places. Jesus and his disciples often slept there, outside in the open air. But, tonight, Jesus asked them not to sleep. 'Stay awake,' he said, 'and pray for me.'

Jesus left them at one end of the garden and went to pray alone. The disciples watched. They had never seen him so upset before. They were tired, though, and, one by one, they fell asleep.

Jesus returned and woke them. 'Stay awake,' he said. 'We've not got long to wait now.'

'What are we waiting for?' they wondered, as Jesus again withdrew to pray. But they did not dare ask.

Peter was determined to keep awake. He had been upset when Jesus said that he would deny he knew Jesus. He would make sure that he did not let Jesus down. But Peter's eyelids were heavy and it was difficult to keep them open. Suddenly, he woke up with a start. He must have dropped off. There was a noise. 'Who's there?' he cried.

'It's only me – Judas.'

Judas walked straight up to Jesus and kissed him.

Jesus looked sad and tears filled his eyes. 'You've betrayed me with a kiss,' he said.

Judas went bright red. 'Here he is!' he yelled to the guards.

Suddenly, there were torches everywhere. Temple guards rushed into the garden and grabbed Jesus. 'You're under arrest!' they shouted.

Peter did not waste a second. He grabbed a sword and swung at one of the guards. He missed his head but cut off his right ear.

'No, Peter, stop!' said Jesus. 'There must be no fighting. I must let them take me away. This is how God wants it to be.' Then he touched the guard's ear and, immediately, it was healed.

The disciples stared at Judas. Judas had been a disciple of Jesus for three years. And now he had become a traitor and betrayed his friend. Jesus had said that one of the disciples would betray him. Now it had come true. Judas had led the temple police right to Jesus.

'Here's your money,' said a guard and gave Judas a purse with 30 pieces of silver in it. Judas ran off into the night.

'Arrest them all!' shouted one of the guards.

The disciples fled in panic. Peter hid in a corner of the garden. He watched the guards march Jesus away, before he crept out and followed them. He wanted to know where they were taking Jesus.

Jesus is sentenced to death

Peter followed the guards to the chief priest's house. They took Jesus inside. Peter waited in the courtyard. It was cold, so Peter went over to the fire, where a group of people were keeping warm.

A man looked at him. 'You're one of Jesus' friends,' he said.

'No, I'm not,' said Peter.

'Are you sure?' asked another.

'Positive,' snapped Peter and left the fire. Things were getting too hot for comfort. He did not want to be arrested as well.

A woman came up to him. 'Hey! You're one of Jesus' disciples, aren't you?' she asked.

'Certainly not,' said Peter, again. Just at that moment, the cock crowed. Peter remembered what Jesus had said. He burst into tears. He had let Jesus down.

The chief priests took Jesus to see Pontius Pilate, the Roman governor. Pilate was not in a good mood. He did not like being got up in the middle of the night. 'Well,' he said. 'What do you want?'

'This man is a blasphemer,' said the chief priest. 'He is claiming to be as important as God. We want you to sentence him to death.'

Pontius Pilate was angry. 'I'm not interested in your religious squabbles. I don't care whether this man is God or not. Has he done anything wrong? Has he committed a crime?'

'Well, he said he could destroy the temple in three days. That's vandalism.'

'You don't sentence a man to death for vandalism,' said Pilate, crossly. 'He needs to be guilty of murder or treason.'

'He's guilty of treason,' the chief priest said. 'He claimed to be the new King of the Jews.'

Pilate turned to Jesus. 'Is that true?' Jesus did not answer. Pilate lost his temper. 'Take him outside and have him whipped. That'll teach him a lesson!'

After whipping him, they brought Jesus back in.

'Well, are you the King of the Jews?' Pilate asked.

'I am,' said Jesus.

But Pilate did not want to have Jesus executed. 'I'll tell you what,' said Pilate. 'Every Passover, we let one prisoner go free. We'll let the crowd choose between Jesus and the murderer, Barabbas.'

The next day, Pilate asked the crowd who they wanted to go free – Jesus or Barabbas. The chief priests told the crowd to shout for Barabbas.

'And what shall I do with Jesus?' Pilate asked the crowd.

'Crucify him!' they shouted.

So Pilate sentenced Jesus to death.

Jesus is crucified

The soldiers led Jesus away.
'So, you're the new King of the Jews!' they jeered. 'Where's your crown?'
One of them had an idea. He made a crown out of a bramble bush. 'Here we are,' he laughed. 'A crown of thorns for the King of the Jews!' Jesus winced with pain, as they pushed the thorns down on to his head.

'He needs a scarlet robe,' they mocked. So one of the soldiers put his cloak round Jesus. 'Now he looks like a king,' and they all laughed at Jesus.

The soldiers made Jesus carry his cross. Jesus was exhausted after being whipped and he stumbled and fell. So they asked a passer-by called Simon to carry it.

They took Jesus to a hill, called Golgotha, just outside the city walls. There, they nailed Jesus' hands and feet to the cross. Above his head, they put a sign, which read, 'The King of the Jews'. On either side of Jesus, they crucified a thief.

Many people came to look at Jesus. 'Hello, your royal highness!' they laughed. Some spat on him. Jesus looked at them and the soldiers who had been so cruel. But Jesus did not hate them. He loved them and forgave them.

All afternoon, Jesus hung on the cross. One of the thieves turned to Jesus. 'You're supposed to be the Messiah,' he said. 'If you're "the Rescuer", why don't you rescue yourself?'

'Shut up!' said the other thief. 'Leave him alone. He's never done anything wrong. He's never done any harm to anyone.' He turned to Jesus. 'Jesus, I believe you're the Messiah – remember me, when you become King.'

Jesus smiled, 'I promise you – tonight you will be with me in heaven.'

Late in the afternoon, the sky turned black. Everything was dark. Jesus cried out in agony. Then he took his last breath and died. The soldiers stuck a spear into Jesus' side to check that he was dead. Then they took his body down from the cross.

A friend of Jesus, called Joseph, took Jesus' body and laid it into a tomb. Mary and some other women, who were friends of Jesus, helped him. The Romans put soldiers to guard the tomb, to make sure no one interfered with it. Then, to make doubly sure, they rolled a huge stone across the entrance of the tomb.

The Resurrection

The disciples sat in silence in the upper room. No one smiled. Only a few days before, they had sat in this room with Jesus, celebrating the Passover. And now, he was dead. They felt lost and lonely and terribly, terribly sad.

'I loved him so much,' said John.

'I thought he was the Messiah, I thought he was going to rescue people,' said Thomas. 'Do you remember how happy we were when he rode into Jerusalem on the donkey? Everybody came out cheering him. They all wanted him to be King – and now he's dead.'

Suddenly, there was a knock on the door. The disciples froze. Perhaps the temple police had come to arrest them.

'Let me in,' said a voice. It was Mary, one of Jesus' friends. They opened the door and let her in. She was so excited, she could hardly speak.

'I've seen him!' she cried. 'I've seen Jesus! He's alive!'

'Don't be silly,' said Thomas. 'You saw him die on the cross.'

'I tell you, he's alive! I've seen him!' she insisted.

'Calm down,' said Peter, gently. 'Tell us what happened.'

Mary began to tell her story.

'We went to the tomb very early this morning, to finish covering the body with spices. When we arrived, the stone had been rolled to one side and the tomb was empty. Then I saw him – in the garden. He spoke to me. He called me "Mary" and told me to come and tell you. He's come back to life.'

Peter did not wait to hear another word – he rushed to the tomb, with John hot on his heels. They raced each other to the tomb and, sure enough, just as Mary had said, they found it empty. And there, in the corner, were the burial clothes.

Peter could hardly believe his eyes. He rushed back to tell the others. 'It's true,' he said, with tears in his eyes, 'Jesus is risen from the dead!'

'Rubbish,' said Thomas. 'I won't believe it unless I actually touch him with my hands.'

Just then, Jesus appeared in the room. The room fell silent. 'Here you are,' Jesus said. 'You can touch me. I'm real. I'm not a ghost. I'm alive.'

'I'm sorry, Jesus,' Thomas said. 'I should have known you could do anything.'

The disciples smiled. It was so good to have Jesus back.

Jesus returns home

After he rose from the dead, the disciples saw Jesus many times. At first, it was strange to have him back. In some ways, he was like a ghost: he could go through walls and he could appear at any time, in the most unexpected places.

One day, two disciples were walking along the road, when Jesus joined them. They did not recognize him at first – not until they got home and had a meal together. When Jesus took the bread and broke it, they realized who it was – it was exactly the same way he had broken bread the night before he died.

In other ways, however, Jesus was not like a ghost at all. One time, he met the disciples when they were fishing and had breakfast with them on the shore. Ghosts certainly do not eat fish for breakfast!

The disciples were thrilled to have him back.

'You won't ever leave us, will you?' asked Peter, one day. 'It was so awful when you died.'

'I don't think I could go through that sort of pain again,' said James, fighting back the tears.

'I have to leave you,' said Jesus. 'I must return to my Father in heaven, where I came from. I have done the job I came to do.' The disciples looked glum. 'But don't be sad. One day, when you die, you will come to be with me. I'll be waiting for you and then we will be together

'It'll never be the same without you,' said Thomas.

'We'll be so lonely on our own,' Peter said.

'You won't be on your
own,' Jesus promised.
'I will send my Holy
Spirit. When I go up to
heaven, he will come to you.
You can't see him or touch him
but otherwise he's just like me.
He will live inside you. He will
stop you feeling lonely and it'll be just
like having me with you all the time. I
promise you – he will never, ever leave you.'
'But I'd rather die tomorrow than live without
you!' cried John. 'Let me come to heaven now.'
'No,' said Jesus. 'You have a job to do. You must
tell people all over the world about me. Tell them how I
came to earth to rescue them and that I love them.'
Jesus led them up to the Mount of Olives, outside
Jerusalem. Then he said to them, 'It is time to leave. Don't be
afraid. Wait for my Holy Spirit, my helper. He'll be coming soon.'
While he was talking, Jesus rose up into the clouds, until the
disciples could no longer see him. They were staring up into the
sky, with their mouths open, when two angels appeared.
'Stop staring,' one said. 'He'll be back one day – when this
world comes to an end and a new one begins.'
So the disciples started back for Jerusalem, to wait for the Holy
Spirit whom Jesus had promised.

93

Jesus sends his helper

As the disciples left the Mount of Olives, they felt sad and puzzled. 'I wish he could have stayed for ever,' said John. 'It won't be the same without him. Life will never be the same again.' They talked about all they had seen: about Jesus disappearing into the clouds and about the angels.

'What shall we do now?' asked Andrew.

'We must do what Jesus told us,' answered Peter. 'We must wait until the Holy Spirit comes.'

So, for the next month, the disciples met together every day, Some of the women, who had been friends of Jesus, joined them. Each day, they prayed to God. And, each day, they waited. But nothing happened and the Holy Spirit did not come.

One day, they were praying together in the upper room, as usual, when the most extraordinary things began to happen. First, there was a very loud noise which sounded like a gale-force wind. The disciples thought the house was about to fall down. Then, what looked like flames came down from the ceiling and landed on the disciples' heads. It looked like their hair was on fire. But not a single hair on their heads was burnt. They felt power, like electricity, go through their bodies and they tingled all over. It felt rather like pins-and-needles, only it was a nice feeling. The Holy Spirit had arrived at last.

The disciples were thrilled. They rushed out of the house and on to the streets. They all started to speak at once. But the oddest thing happened. They all spoke in foreign languages they didn't know.

'What's going on?' asked people from all over the world, who had come to a festival. 'How come these people know so many of our languages?'

Some of them laughed, 'They're talking gibberish – they must be drunk!'

But Peter stood up and explained. 'We're not drunk,' he said, 'but we are excited!' And he told them all about Jesus, 'the Rescuer.' He told them how Jesus had died and then come back to life. How he had gone up to heaven and how he had promised his Holy Spirit would come down. 'And today he has,' said Peter. 'The Holy Spirit has come down and now he is living inside us. And that's how we can speak in different languages.'

And, from that day on, the disciples went around telling people the story of Jesus and how he had rescued the world from sin. They did many miracles, some strange things happened to them and they had many adventures.

But, wherever they went, Jesus went with them. His Spirit lived in them. And they knew, that from then on, wherever they went, whatever they did, they would never, ever be alone. For Jesus had promised, he would always be with them.

Jesus said, 'Let the little children come
to me and don't get in their way.
Because the Kingdom of God belongs
to little children. Whoever wants to
enter the Kingdom of God must come
like a little child.'
Then he took them in his arms and
embraced them.

Mark 10: 14